PEARSON

ALWAYS LEARNING

Digital Communication Laboratory Manual Using VisSim

Prepared by M. Tavakoli

Custom Edition

Pearson Learning Solutions, 501 Boylston Street, Suite 900, Boston, MA 02116
A Pearson Education Company
www.pearsoned.com

Printed in the United States of America

¦ 4 5 6 7 8 9 10 V202 16 15 14 13 12 11

000200010270803832

RG

ISBN 10: 1-256-41378-X
ISBN 13: 978-1-256-41378-3

TABLE OF CONTENTS

Introduction: Getting Started

About this Edition of Lab Manual

This lab manual was written for the student studying the first course in Digital Communication using VisSim simulation software. No prior knowledge of the technical aspect of VisSim is assumed.

The first chapter is a quick reference for the basic operation of VisSim and is copied from different parts of the software's Help menu. Use Help to get more information about the software.

The following chapters use step-by-step simulation and teach the functions of different blocks for more elaborate simulation.

A brief description of each block is given from Help when a block is used for the first time, and its typical applications are explained.

The manual encourages students to individually write their conclusions from each exercise by themselves prints them along with a copy of the simulation, and submit everything to their instructors. This approach makes students think about what they are learning from each task.

In this edition in order to make the lab simulations easier for students the following changes have been made in the lab manual.

1. Figures have been redrawn in VisSim and make them more readable.
2. The location of each block in the library has been provided
3. The parameters needed for each block have been added
4. The parameters for running the simulation properties have been included.
5. Make all simulations compatible with VisSim. In this newer version of the software several blocks were modified to use external clock pulse to improve efficiency of the simulation.
6. More labs are added for those interested students if they want to simulate more communication systems.

The location each block can be found from the introduction (Getting started) and also the location is given in each lab exercise.

Acknowledgement

I am grateful to Dr. Steve Shen the National chair of School of Electronic Technology curriculum manager for his support through this project.

I would like also to thank Dr. Atoussa H. Tehrani chair, school of electronic technology at ITT Fort Lauderdale for her support and suggestions.

I like also to thank the Pearson team especially Jenny Wright and the project manager Dainelle Baughman that made this publication possible.

All comments are welcome and are hereby gratefully acknowledged.
Mohamad Tavakoli
ITT Technical Institute
Tempe, Arizona
E-mail: mtavakoli@itt-tech.edu

Digital Communication Lab Manual: Using VisSim

Introduction: Getting Started*

1.1 Introduction

Welcome to VisSim. Previous version of the software is called Commsim. VisSim provides the ideal solution for designing and simulating analog and digital end-to-end communication links. The VisSim library supports digital and analog modulation, channel models, demodulation, phase locked loops, error correcting codes, and bit error rate analysis to mention a few.

Through its support of complex math, VisSim enables the use of complex envelope simulations. By using low pass equivalent models, communication engineers can significantly reduce the computing load required to support most communication analysis problems.

1.2 A Typical Communication Link

A typical communication link includes, at a minimum, three key elements: a transmitter, a communication medium or channel, and a receiver. The ability to simulate all three of these elements is required in order to successfully model any end-to-end communication system.

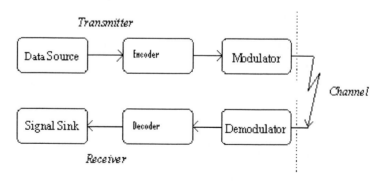

Figure 1.1 A typical communication system

The transmitter and receiver elements can in turn be subdivided into further sub-systems, as shown in the preceding figure. These include a data source (analog or

---

*"A Typical Communication Link," reprinted from *Commsim 7 tutorial*. Copyright © 2004 Electronics Workbench.

digital), an optional data encoder, a modulator, a demodulator, an optional data decoder, and a signal sink.

The data source generates the information signal that is intended to be sent to a particular receiver. This signal can be either an analog signal such as speech, or a digital signal such as a binary data sequence. This signal is typically a base band signal represented by a voltage level.

For analog signals, it is often desirable to digitally encode the signal prior to transmission by undergoing a quantization process. This step converts the analog signal into a digital signal. While some information is lost in this process, the resulting digital signal is often far less susceptible to the effects of noise in the transmission channel.

An encoder can also be used to add redundancy to a digital data stream, in the form of additional data bits, in a way that provides an error correction capability at the receiver. This overall process is referred to as Forward Error Correction (FEC). Among the most popular FEC schemes are convolution coding, block coding and trellis coding. It is important to note that usually the output bit rate of an encoder is not equal to the input bit rate. To properly distinguish between the two bit rates, the transmitter's input rate is referred to as the information data rate, while the transmitter output rate is referred to as the channel data rate.

Depending on the type of information signal and the particular transmission medium, different modulation techniques are employed. Modulation refers to the specific technique used to represent the information signal as it is physically transmitted to the receiver. For example, in Amplitude Modulation (AM), the information is represented by amplitude variations of the carrier signal.

Once the signal is modulated, it is sent through a transmission medium, also known as a channel, to reach the intended receiver. This may be a copper wire, coax cable, or the atmosphere in the case of a radio transmission. To some extent, all channels introduce some form of distortion to the original signal. Many different channel models have been developed to mathematically represent such distortions. A commonly used channel model is the Additive White Gaussian Noise (AWGN) channel. In this channel, noise with uniform power spectral density (hence the term "white") is assumed to be added to the information signal. Other types of channels include fading channels and multipath channels.

When the transmitted signal reaches the intended receiver, it undergoes a demodulation process. This step is the opposite of modulation and refers to the process required to extract the original information signal from the modulated signal. Demodulation also includes any steps associated with signal synchronization, such as the use of phase locked loops in achieving phase coherence between the incoming signal and the receiver's local oscillator.

When data encoding is included at the transmitter, a data-decoding step must be performed prior to recovering the original data signal. The signal decoding process is usually more complicated than the encoding process and can be very computationally intensive. Efficient decoding schemes, however, have been developed over the years—one example is the Viterbi decoding algorithm, which is used to decode convolutionally encoded data.

Finally, an estimate of the original signal is produced at the output of the receiver. The receiver's output port is sometimes referred to as the signal sink. As communications engineers, we are usually interested in knowing how well the source information was recreated at the receiver's output. Several metrics are used by engineers to evaluate the success of the data transmission. The most common metric, in the case of digital signals, is the received Bit Error Rate (BER). Other valuable performance indicators include the received Signal to Noise Ratio (SNR), eye patterns and phase scatter plots to name a few.

1.3 Starting VisSim

This procedure describes the start-up method for VisSim.

1. Click on Start > Programs > VisSim
2. Or double-click on the VisSim icon

1.4 Creating a New Block Diagram

To open a new diagram, choose the File > New command. If you're working on a different diagram and haven't yet saved your changes, VisSim prompts you to save them, and then creates a new diagram. VisSim temporarily names the diagram Diagram1. The first time you attempt to save it, VisSim asks for a new name.

1.5 Opening an Existing Block Diagram

You can easily open any of the last 12 block diagrams you worked on. When you click on the File menu, VisSim displays their names at the bottom of the menu.

To open any block diagram, choose the File > Open command. If another diagram is currently opened and contains unsaved changes, VisSim asks you if you want them saved before it closes the diagram and displays the File Open dialog box.

When you assign a title to a block diagram using the Diagram Information command, the title appears in the File Open dialog box when you select the block diagram.

1.6 To Open a Block Diagram

1. Choose File > Open.
2. In the File Name box, type or select the name of the block diagram you want to open. If you do not see the block diagram you want, select a new drive or directory.
3. To open the block diagram for viewing only, activate the Read Only parameter. Although you can edit the block diagram, you must save the diagram under a new name to retain your edits.
4. Click on the OK button, or press ENTER.

1.7 Undoing an Editing Action

If you make a change to a block diagram then decide against the change, use the Edit > Undo command to erase it. If the Undo command is dimmed, the effect of the command cannot be undone.

1.8 Saving a Block Diagram

When you open a block diagram, VisSim reads the diagram into your computer's memory. As you work on the diagram, the changes you make are temporary. To make the changes permanent, you must save them to disk.

To save an existing block diagram:

■   Choose File > Save.

To save a block diagram under a new name:

You can use File > Save As to save the block diagram under a new name or to a different directory or device. This command comes in handy when you want to alter the current diagram but keep its original version.

1.9 Printing a Block Diagram

The File > Print command lets you choose a printer and select printing options, such as the number of copies, the layers to be printed, and so on.

To print a diagram:

1. Choose File > Print.
2. Choose File > printer setup

    -To setup paper size, Orientation

3. Choose File > Page setup

    - To fit diagram to page, tile printed page for large diagram, orientation, margin and paper

4. Choose File > print preview

    - To preview the print

1.10 Wiring Basics

By wiring blocks together, VisSim is able to pass signals among blocks during a simulation. Signals are simply data. Input signals (x_n) represent data entering blocks; output signals (y_n) represent data exiting blocks.

VisSim offers two types of wires:

- flexWires

- vector wires

A flexWire is a thin wire that allows a single signal to pass through it. A vector wire, on the other hand, is a thick wire that contains multiple flexWires. Typically, you use vector wires when performing vector or matrix operations, or to reduce wiring clutter at top-level diagram design.

The table below lists the blocks that accept vector wires:

Block category	Block name
Annotation	index, scalarToVec, variable, vecToScalar, wirePositioner
Arithmetic	1/X, -X, *, /, abs, convert, gain, power, sign, summing Junction, unit Conversion
MatLab Interface	MatLab Expression, MatLab Read Variable, MatLab Write Variable
Matrix Operations	buffer, dot Product, fft, ifft, inverse, multiply, transpose, vsum
Nonlinear	case, merge
Signal Consumer	display

You can manually bundle and unbundle flexWires using the scalarToVec and vecToScalar blocks.

You can alternatively use variable block which is located at Block > annotation > Variable to pass signals. A variable lets you name and transmit a signal throughout a block diagram without using wires. Typically, you use a variable block for system-wide variables or signals that would be laborious or visually messy to represent as wires. For more information, click on Variable block and then click help and then click **Using variables to pass signals.**

1.11 Wiring Blocks Together

You attach flexWires and vector wires to blocks through their connector tabs. Once you have attached a wire to a block, VisSim maintains the connection even as you move the block around the screen.

When you wire blocks, the following rules are in effect:

- Wires can only be drawn between an input and output connector tab pair. The triangular shape of the connector tab lets you easily distinguish inputs from outputs.

- Input connector tabs can only have one wire attached to them; output connector tabs can have any number of wires attached to them. To change the number of connector tabs on a block, do the following:

To add or remove connector tabs

1. Do one of the following:

   - From the toolbar, choose ⊞ or ⊞.
   - Choose Edit > Add Connector or Edit > Remove Connector.

2. Do one of the following:

To	Do this
Add a connector tab	Point to where you want the tab. The short black line indicates tab placement. Then click the mouse.
Delete a connector tab	Point to the tab to be deleted. The selected tab has a short black line over it. Then click the mouse.

3. Repeat step 2 for as many tabs that you want to add or delete.

4. Click the mouse on empty screen space to exit this command.

▓ Hold Control and right click on input to toggle sign from "+" to "-"

▓ If you draw multiple wires between two blocks, VisSim automatically skews them.

1.12 To Wire Blocks

1. Point to a connector tab on one of the blocks to be wired. The pointer becomes a ↑.

2. Hold down the mouse button and drag the pointer over the connector tab on the destination block. As you drag the pointer, VisSim generates a shimmering line, which represents the wire. Because VisSim draws lines vertically and horizontally, the path of the line may not mimic the path of the cursor.

3. Release the mouse button.

1.13 Creating a Specific Wiring Path

Using wirePositioner block which is located at Blocks > Annotation > Wire positioning, you can perform a connect-the-dot method of wiring. That is, you insert wirePositioner blocks and then manually route the wire through them. Since you control the placement of the wirePositioner blocks, it's easy to draw a precise wiring path.

Additionally, because wirePositioner blocks do not take any additional computation time, you won't see a decrease in performance during a simulation.

Both flexWires and vector wires can by routed through wirePositioner blocks.

1.14 Deleting Wires

You delete a wire by detaching it from an input connector tab.

1. Point to the tab.
2. Hold down the mouse button as you drag the pointer away from the tab.
3. Release the mouse button.

1.15 Selecting a Block

1. Point to the block.
2. Click the mouse Move the block to desired position and click the mouse

1.16 Moving and Copying Blocks

Moving and copying blocks are common operations you'll perform in VisSim. Like many operations, there are several ways to move and copy blocks. For instance, you can move blocks by dragging and dropping them into place or you can cut them to the Windows Clipboard. From there, you can paste them back into your diagram or into another VisSim diagram. You can also paste them into other Windows-based applications.

Rules for moving and copying blocks: The following rules are in effect when you're moving and copying blocks:

-   Moved and copied blocks retain the parameter values of the original blocks.
-   Moved and copied blocks retain their internal wiring. This means that wires connecting blocks within the group of copied or cut blocks are retained.

- Moved and copied blocks lose their peripheral wiring. This means that wires connecting blocks in the group of blocks being copied or cut to other blocks are not retained.

- When moving or copying a compound block containing a global variable block with input, VisSim appends a number to the variable block name to keep it unique.

Drag-and-drop editing: An easy way to move or copy blocks within the current level of the diagram is with drag-and-drop editing. If you're moving or copying blocks to another level in the diagram, or to a different block diagram, you have to use the Edit menu's Cut, Copy, and Paste commands.

Copying, cutting, and pasting blocks: The Copy, Cut, and Paste commands use the Windows Clipboard to transfer blocks to another block diagram level or to a different block diagram. You can also use the Clipboard to paste blocks into other applications.

The Clipboard can only hold one selection of cut or copied blocks at a time. If you place a new selection in the Clipboard, it overwrites whatever was already there.

1.17 Flipping Blocks

By allowing you to flip blocks 180°, VisSim can present a more logical representation of right-to-left signal flow. When you flip blocks, VisSim redraws all flexWires attached to the blocks.

To flip a block:

1. Select the blocks to be flipped.
2. Click the right mouse button over a selected block and choose Flip Horizontal from the pop-up menu.
3. Click the mouse on empty screen space to unselect the blocks.

1.18 Finding Blocks

When you choose the Find command, VisSim displays a dialog box you can use to specify the block, label, or text string you want to find. If you want to search for variables, you can also click on the DOWN ARROW next to the Find What box and select a variable name from the entries. All variable blocks in the diagram are listed in the drop-down list.

Once VisSim finds the search item, you can make a change in the diagram and then continue the search by choosing the Find Next button. The dialog box stays open so you can edit the diagram. To move the dialog box out of the way, drag on its title bar.

1.19 To Find a Block:

1. Choose Edit > Find.
2. In the Find What box, enter the search item. If you're searching for a variable, you can also click on the DOWN ARROW next to the Find What box and select from the variables list.
3. Select any option you want to control the search.
4. Choose the Find Next button. When VisSim finds a match, it highlights the block in black.
5. To cancel a search or close the dialog box, choose the Cancel button.

1.20 Deleting Blocks

When your block diagram contains blocks you no longer need, you can delete them using the Edit > Clear command or the DEL key. One Block command. When you use these commands, all wires attached to the deleted blocks are also deleted.

To clear selected blocks:

1. Select the blocks to be cleared.
2. Choose Edit > Cut or press DEL.

1.21 Creating a Compound Block

When you create a compound block, VisSim attaches connector tabs to the compound block for each of the following situations:

■ All unsatisfied connector tabs on the internal blocks (except global variables)

■ All satisfied connector tabs to external blocks

To create a compound block:

1. Select the blocks to be encapsulated.
2. Choose Edit > Create Compound Block.
3. Under compound name, enter a name. Avoid using the dot (.) character in the name; VisSim uses it to separate compound block names in the title bar. The default name is Compound.
4. Click on the OK button, or press ENTER.

1.22 Setting Up Block Properties

Most blocks have user-settable properties associated with them that allow you to set simulation invariant parameters of the blocks' functions. You define and change property values for a block through its Properties dialog box. When you change a property while the simulation is running, VisSim immediately updates the simulation to reflect the change. Initial conditions, which are supplied to the system at the start of a simulation, are also set in the blocks via their Properties dialog boxes.

1.23 To Set Up Block Properties:

1. Choose Edit > Block Properties.
2. Point to the block whose parameters you want to define or change and click the mouse.
3. In the Properties dialog box, enter or select the new parameter values and options, and then choose the OK button, or press ENTER.

A shortcut for accessing Properties dialog boxes for most blocks is to click the right mouse button over the block. For button, compound, DDE, DDEsend, DDEreceive, embed, label, user Function, and variable blocks, hold down the CTRL key while you click the right mouse button to access their Properties dialog boxes.

1.24 To Find Information on Each Block:

1. Point to the block whose information you want to find and click the mouse.
2. In the Properties dialog box, select **Help** .

1.25 Setting Simulation Range

Setting up the simulation range involves choosing the start and end of the simulation, specifying the step size of the integration algorithm, indicating whether VisSim runs in real-time mode, and indicating whether VisSim automatically restarts the simulation either with or without the last known system states.

To set up the Simulation Range options:

1. Choose System > System Properties.
2. Click on the Range tab.

   The Range sheet in the Simulation Properties dialog box appears.
3. Choose the options you want, then click on the OK button, or press ENTER.

1.26 Plotting

The plot block displays data in a two-dimensional time domain plot. You can customize the plot and control how data is in the following ways:

- Choose between XY or frequency domain
- Select logarithmic scaling, fixed axis bounds, or a time axis scale
- Display signal traces as individual data points, line segments, or stepped line segments
- Overlay signal traces with geometric markers
- Specify the number of data points to plot
- Use crosshairs and grid lines to determine data point coordinates
- Overlap plots

You can also save simulation data to file in .DAT, .M, .MAT, and .WAV formats.

1.27 Printing a Plot Block

To print just a plot, click on the control-menu box in the upper left-hand corner of the plot and select the Print command.

1.28 Labeling

Block Category: Blocks > Annotation > label

The label block lets you insert floating labels in a block diagram. You can choose the text attributes for the label, as well as a colored background. The label block is particularly useful for tagging signals.

Most block dialog boxes let you enter a label for the block. To display these labels, turn on the View > Block Labels command.

To continue a label to a new line, hold down the CTRL key while you simultaneously press the ENTER key.

Click on the Background Color button to select a background color for the label. Click on the Fonts button to select a font, font style, point size, color, and special effects for the text. A sample of the text is displayed in the Sample box.

To override the selections in the View > Colors and View > Fonts dialog boxes, activate Override Default Colors and Override Default Font, respectively.

1.29 Comm. Block Set

The following will help you to find blocks in different categories.

1.29.1 Channel Category

☐ Binary Symmetric Channel

☐ Jakes Mobile

☐ Mobile Fading

☐ AWGN (Complex)

☐ AWGN (Real)

☐ Multipath

☐ Propagation Loss

☐ TWTA Channel

☐ Vector AWGN

☐ Rice/Rayleigh Fading

☐ Rummler Multipath

1.29.2 Complex Math

☐ Complex Addition

☐ Complex Conjugate

☐ Complex Inverse

☐ Complex Multiplication

☐ Complex Power

☐ Complex Division

☐ Magnitude/Phase to Complex

☐ Complex Square Root

☐ Complex to Magnitude/Phase

☐ Complex to Real/Imaginary

☐ Real/Imaginary to Complex

1.29.3 Modulators

a) <u>Complex</u>

☐ GFSK

☐ GMSK

☐ AM

☐ Differential PSK

☐ Fm

☐ FSK

☐ I/Q

☐ MSK

☐ PM

☐ PSK

☐ QAM/PAM

☐ SQPSK

b) <u>Real</u>

☐ AM (Re)

☐ Differential PSK (Re)

☐ FM (Re)

☐ FSK (Re)

☐ I/Q (Re)

☐ MSK (Re)

☐ PM (Re)

☐ PPM

☐ PSK (Re)

☐ QAM/PAM (Re)

☐ SQPSK (Re)

1.29.4 Demodulators

☐ DQPSK Detector

☐ FM Demodulator

☐ IQ Detector

☐ PPM Demodulator

☐ PSK Detector

☐ QAM/PAM Detector

1.29.5 Digital

☐ Binary Counter

☐ Bits to Symbol

☐ Buffer

☐ D Flip Flop

☐ Divide by N

☐ JK Flip Flop

☐ Mux/Demux

☐ Parallel to Serial

☐ Queue

☐ Serial to Parallel

☐ Symbol to Bits

☐ Unbuffer

1.29.6 Encode/Decode

☐ Block Interleaver

- ☐ Convolutional Encoder
- ☐ Convolutional Interleaver
- ☐ Depuncture
- ☐ Gray Map
- ☐ Gray Reverse Map
- ☐ Puncture
- ☐ Reed-Solomon Decoder
- ☐ Reed-Solomon Encoder
- ☐ Trellis Decoder
- ☐ Trellis Encoder
- ☐ Turbo Code Decoder
- ☐ Turbo Code Encoder
- ☐ Viterbi Decoder (Hard)
- ☐ Viterbi Decoder (Soft)

1.29.7 Estimators

- ☐ Average Power
- ☐ Bit Error Rate
- ☐ BER Curve Control
- ☐ Correlation
- ☐ Delay Estimator
- ☐ Event Time
- ☐ Mean
- ☐ Median
- ☐ Variance
- ☐ Weighted Mean

1.29.8 Filters

- ☐ Adaptive Equalizer
- ☐ File FIR Filter
- ☐ Obsolete Gaussian FIR Filter
- ☐ FIR Filter
- ☐ IIR Filter

- Pulse Shaping Filter
- Sampling File FIR
- Sampling FIR Filter
- MagPhase Filter

1.29.9 Operators

- A/D Converter
- Compander
- Complex Exponential
- Complex FFT/IFFT
- Conversions
- Decimation
- Delay (Complex)
- Delay (Real)
- Gain (dB)
- Integrate & Dump
- IQ Mapper
- Max Index
- Modulo
- Oscilloscope (Core)
- Phase Rotate
- Phase Unwrap
- Polynomial
- Spectrum (Complex or Real)
- Vector FFT
- Vector Merge

1.29.10 PLL

- Charge Pump
- Loop Filter (2nd Order PLL)
- Loop Filter (3rd Order PLL)
- Type-2 Phase Detector
- Type-3 Phase Detector

☐ Type-4 Phase Detector

1.29.11 RF

☐ Amplifier

☐ Attenuator

☐ Coupler

☐ Double Balanced Mixer

☐ Splitter/Combiner

☐ Switch

☐ Variable Attenuator

1.29.12 Signal Sources

☐ Complex Tone

☐ File Data

☐ Frequency Sweep

☐ Impulse

☐ Impulse Train

☐ Noise

☐ PN Sequence

☐ Obsolete Random Seed

☐ Random Symbol Source

☐ Rectangular Pulses

☐ Sinusoid

☐ Spectral Mask

☐ Voltage Controlled Oscillator

☐ Walsh Sequence

☐ Waveform Generator

☐ Vector Constant

1.30 Block Reference

The following help you to find different blocks in different categories.

1.30.1 Animation

animate

lineDraw

1.30.2 Annotation

bezel

comment

date

label

scalarToVec

vecToScalar

variable

wirePositioner

1.30.3 Arithmetic

1/X (inverse)

* (multiply)

-X (negate)

/ (divide)

abs

unitConversion

convert

gain

pow

sign

summing Junction

1.30.4 Boolean

< (less than)

<= (less than or equal to)

== (equal to)

!= (not equal to)

> (greater than)

>= (greater than or equal to)

and

not

or

xor

1.30.5 DDE

DDEreceive

DDEsend

1.30.6 Integration

integrator (1/S)

limitedIntegrator (1/S)

resetIntegrator (1/S)

1.30.7 Linear System

stateSpace

transferFunction

1.30.8 Matrix Operation

buffer

dotProduct

fft

ifft

index

invert

multiply

psd

transpose

vsum

1.30.9 Nonlinear

case

crossDetect

deadband

int

limit

map

max

merge

min

quantize

relay

sample Hold

1.30.10 Optimization

constraint

cost

global Constraint

parameter Unknown

unknown

1.30.11 Random Generator

Gaussian

uniform

PRBS

1.30.12 Real Time

ActiveX read

ActiveX write

About active x interface

1.30.13 Signal Consumer

display

error

export

histogram

Light

meter

plot

stop

strip Chart

1.30.14 Signal Producer

button

const

dialog Constant

import

parabola

pulse Train

ramp

real-time

sinusoid

slider

step

1.30.15 Time Delay

timeDelay

unitDelay

1.30.16 Transcendental

acos

asin

atan2

Bessel

cos

cosh

exp

ln

log10

sin

sinh

sqrt

tan

tanh

sin

sinh

sqrt

tan

tanh

1.30.17 Embedded

1.30.18 User Function

1.30.19 Expression

1.30.20 OLEobject

1.31 Wireless

801.11

802.11a/g

802.11b

Bluetooth

Generic

Ultrawidwband

1.32 Simulation Basics

VisSim can simulate linear, nonlinear, continuous, and discrete systems. VisSim can also simulate systems containing both continuous and discrete transfer functions, as well as systems containing multi-rate sampling for discrete transfer functions.

When you initiate a simulation, VisSim first evaluates Signal Producer blocks, like consts and ramps, then sends the data to intermediate blocks that have both inputs and outputs, like gains and summing Junctions. Lastly, it sends data to Signal Consumer blocks that have only inputs, such as plots and meters.

VisSim simulates a system according to:

■ Simulation parameters set in the dialog box for the System > System Properties command

■ Initial conditions for the system set in the applicable blocks

If View < status bar is turned on, VisSim displays current settings for the simulation range, step size, elapsed simulation time, integration algorithm, and implicit solver.

1.33 Controlling a Simulation

There are two ways to control a simulation:

■ Using the Simulate menu Go, Stop, Continue, and Reset Sim commands or corresponding toolbar buttons

■ Using the simulation Control Panel

Both ways provide the same level of interactive control over the simulation.

1.33.1 The Control Panel

Use the Control Panel

The Control Panel provides fast and easy interactive control over a simulation.

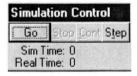

To Activate the Control Panel

■ Choose View > Control Panel

Go

Starts a simulation. It is equivalent to the Go command in the Simulate menu, and the button in the toolbar.

Stop

Stops a simulation. It is equivalent to the Stop command in the Simulate menu, and the button in the toolbar.

Cont

Continues a stopped simulation. It is equivalent to the Continue command in the Simulate menu, and the button in the toolbar.

Step

Single-steps through a simulation. Each time you press the Step pushbutton, the simulation advances one time step. The Step pushbutton is equivalent to button in the toolbar.

Reset

When you're single-stepping or proceeding normally through a simulation, the Go pushbutton is replaced with the Reset pushbutton. If you click on Reset, VisSim resets the system to its initial conditions.

1.33.2 To Start a Simulation

Do one of the following:

- From the toolbar, choose .
- From the Control Panel, press the Go pushbutton.
- Choose System > Go command.

1.33.3 To Stop a Simulation

Do one of the following:

- From the toolbar, choose .
- From the Control Panel, press the Stop pushbutton.

■ Choose System > Stop.

1.33.4 To Continue a Simulation

Do one of the following:

■ From the toolbar, choose ⬚

■ From the Control Panel, press the Cont pushbutton.

■ Choose System > Continue.

1.33.5 To Single-Step a Simulation

Do one of the following:

■ From the toolbar, choose ⬚

■ From the Control Panel, press the Step pushbutton.

1.33.6 To Reset a Simulation

Do one of the following:

■ From the Control Panel, press the Reset pushbutton.

■ Choose System > Reset Sim.

Lab 1: Wiring, Sources, Displays and Simulation properties

Exercise 1

Objective

To learn how to connect blocks and display sinusoid function block

Lab Setup

Standard lab setup with VisSim installed

Introduction

The sinusoid block in Comm > Signal sources > Sinusoid generate a sine wave at the specified frequency. The amplitude can be specified either in volts or dBm level (50 ohms impedance).

Procedure

1. Simulate the following system using VisSim.

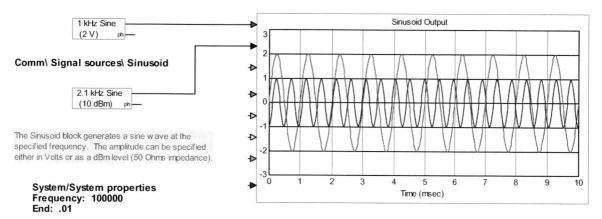

Block -> Signal consumer-> Plot

Setting Block Options for Plot

Plot block is located in Block > Signal consumer > Plot or you can click on the plot toolbar button on the upper part of VisSim window.

The Option property sheet in the Plot Properties dialog box lets you choose between XY and frequency domain plots; select logarithmic scaling, fixed axis bounds, or a time axis scale; display signal traces as individual data points, line segments, or stepped line segments; and more.

To access the Options property sheet:

Double click on the plot or in general:

a) Choose Edit > Block Properties.

b) Click the mouse over the plot block.

c) Click on the Options tab.

The Options sheet in the Plot Properties dialog box appears.

d) Choose the options you want; then click the OK button, or press ENTER.

These options include:

Fixed Bound

Specifies the region of the plot you want to view by letting you select the plotting bounds. When Fixed Bound is activated, VisSim uses the values for the X Upper Bound, X Lower Bound, Y Upper Bound, and Y Lower Bound parameters in the Axis property sheet. In this exercise the Y bound is set between -3 to +3

Grid Line

Grid lines extend from the vertical and horizontal axis coordinates. Grid frequency of the vertical and horizontal spacing of grid lines is controlled by the spacing of the axis coordinates. VisSim automatically establishes reasonable axis coordinate spacing and hence controls the grid frequency.

Plot Settings for this Exercise

a) Options

-Fixed bound

-Grid line

b) Axis

-Y upper	3
-Y lower	-3
-X upper	10
-X lower	0

c) Label

-Title:	Sinusoid output
-X label	Time (msec)

-Timing Scale   Millisecond

Sine: Comm > Signal Sources > Sinusoid

The sinusoid block generates a sine wave at the specified frequency. The amplitude can be specified either in Volt or as a dBm level (50 ohm impedance).

Simulation Properties

These options include:

Click on System > System properties

a) *Range*

-Frequency	100,000 (Do not use , in the dialog box)
-End	0.01

The rest are set by default.

2. Change the simulation frequency to 10,000 and then 1,000. Explain the effects on the output by using a label box (Block > Annotation > label) in your simulated output.

3. Change the frequency of input sine waves to 1Hz and 2 Hz. Change the plot properties to draw one complete cycles of the 1Hz and two complete cycle of the 2 Hz input (For more information about plot properties, double click on plot, then click on Help).

    Notice that as the frequency of input signal gets lower the range of frequency setting in Simulation properties could be lowered.

4. Type your conclusion on your simulation using a label box which is located in Block > Annotation >label. Print a copy of your simulation for your instructor.

Exercise 2

Objective

To plot the output of periodic square waves, triangle waves, and saw-toothed waves

Lab Setup

Standard lab setup with VisSim installed

Procedure

1. Simulate the following system using VisSim.
   A constant block with the value of -3 is used in this system. Constant block is in the Block > signal producer. The cont block is also located on the toolbar of VisSim window.The constant block is added via a summing junction (Block > Arithmetic > summing junction) to the clock output of the square wave signal. This is a useful way to separate two signal output on the plot by any value through the constant block. Since the signal for display is low frequency, in simulation properties the frequency is set to 100.

   The waveform generator is located in Comm > Signal sources > Waveform generator. The waveform block generates periodic pulses, to include square waves, triangle waves and saw tooth waves.

Comm/ Signal sources/Waveform generator

The Waveform block generates
periodic pulse trains, to include:
- Square Waves
- Triangle Waves
- Sawtooth Waves

Simulation:
System > System Properties
Frequency : 100
End: 5

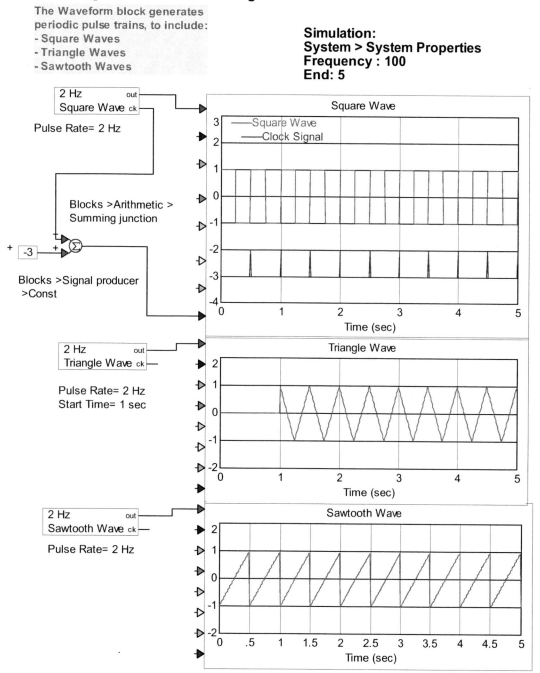

2 Hz   out
Square Wave ck

Pulse Rate= 2 Hz

Blocks >Arithmetic >
Summing junction

Blocks >Signal producer
>Const

2 Hz   out
Triangle Wave ck

Pulse Rate= 2 Hz
Start Time= 1 sec

2 Hz   out
Sawtooth Wave ck

Pulse Rate= 2 Hz

Block-> Signal consumer ->PLot

2. Explain why const block is used in this simulation. Write your explanation by using a label in your simulation blocks, and print a copy of your output for your instructor.

3. Change the frequency of the input waves to 2 KHz, and plot the outputs. Remember you have to increase the frequency of simulation to much higher value than 100, in system properties dialog box.

4. Change the constant block to +3, and write down your observation.

Exercise 3

Objective

To generate rectangular pulses with different pulse rate and duty cycle

Lab Setup

Standard lab setup with VisSim installed

Procedure

1. Simulate the following system using VisSim.

   The rectangular pulse block (Comm > Signal sources > Rectangular pulse) generates a periodic pulse train and allows the specification of:

   Pulse rate, Duty cycle, High level, Low level, and Start time.

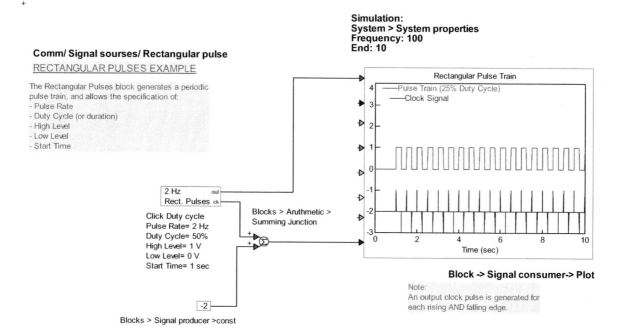

Notice that an output clock pulse is generated for each rising and falling edge.

As you see in this figure in order to separate output from clock, constant block in conjunction with summing junction is used.

The purpose of Constant block (Blocks > Signal producer) > Const) and Summing junction (Blocks > Arithmetic > Summing Junction) is explained in previous exercise.

2. Generate a rectangular pulse with the following properties:
    -   Pulse rate = 5 Hz
    -   Duty cycle = 25%
    -   High level = 1 V
    -   Low level = 0 V
    -   Start Time = 0 sec

3. Print a copy of your simulation for your instructor.

Exercise 4

Objective

To generate a single impulse as well as an impulse train and to study Max Plotted Points properties in a Plot Block

Lab Setup

Standard lab setup with VisSim installed

Procedure

1. Simulate the following system using VisSim.

   To avoid missing impulse events in a Plot block output due to unwanted data decimation during plotting, make sure that in the Plot block Max Plot Points setting is 0.

   Notice the dropouts in a lower plot. In Plot properties, under Options, the Max Plotted Points for this plot is set to 256.

   The default number of points for new plot blocks can be set under the Default tab in the Simulate/simulation Properties menu.

2. Location of the Blocks'

   a) **Impulse**: Comm > Signal Sources > Impulse

   b) **Impulse Train**: Comm > Signal Sources > Impulse train

   c) **Plot:** Use Toolbar button

3. **Simulation properties**:

   System > System properties

   a) Frequency: 100

   b) End: 10

Simulate:
System -> System properties
Frequency: 100
End: 10

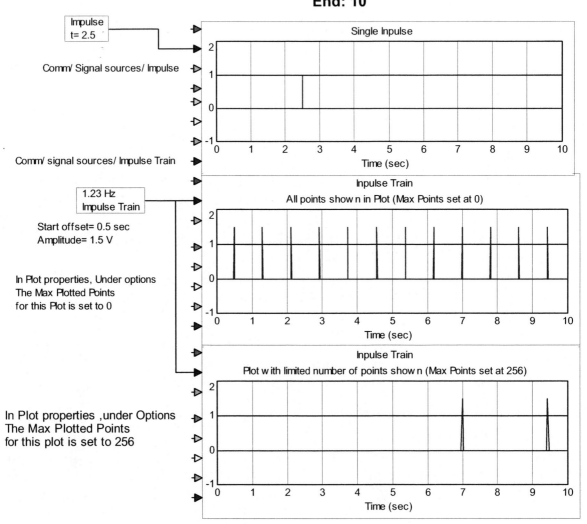

Impulse
t= 2.5

Comm/ Signal sources/ Impulse

Comm/ signal sources/ Impulse Train

1.23 Hz
Impulse Train

Start offset= 0.5 sec
Amplitude= 1.5 V

In Plot properties, Under options
The Max Plotted Points
for this Plot is set to 0

In Plot properties ,under Options
The Max Plotted Points
for this plot is set to 256

Block-> Signal consumer ->PLot

4. For a lower plot, change the Max Plotted Points (in Plot properties, under Options) to different values (for example 400, 500). Observe and write down the effects by using a label in your simulation.

5. Print a copy of your simulation and type your conclusion.

Exercise 5

Objective

To show the Operators/Conversion block

Lab Setup

Standard lab setup with VisSim installed

Conversion Block

Block Category: Comm > Operators > Conversion block

This block implements many common conversions. The desired conversion is selected by choosing the appropriate radio button in the block's setup dialog box.

Real/Imag to Mag/Phase

Converts a complex input represented in Real/Imaginary format to Magnitude/Phase format

Mag/Phase to Real/Imag

Converts a complex input represented in Magnitude/Phase format to Real/Imaginary format

Real to Decibels

Converts a real input to decibels. The input must be greater than zero

Decibels to Real

Converts a decibel input to a real number

Power to Decibels

Converts a power input value to decibels. The input must be greater than zero

Decibels to Power

Converts a decibel input to a power value

Hertz to Rad/sec

Converts from hertz to radians/second

Rad/sec to Hertz

Converts from radians/second to hertz

Degrees to Radians

Converts from degrees to radians

Radians to Degrees

Converts from radians to degrees

Display Block

Blocks > Signal Consumer > Display

Or find it in the toolbar button of VisSim window

The display block displays the current value of the input signal in any number of significant digits. You can select a color for the displayed value as well as a background color for the block.

Const Block

Blocks > Signal producer > Const

Procedure

1. Simulate the following system using VisSim. All examples shown in this figure are using conversion blocks and display

2. **Simulation Properties**:

System > System properties

a) Frequency 100

b) End 10

Simulation:
System > System Properties
Frequency: 100
End:10

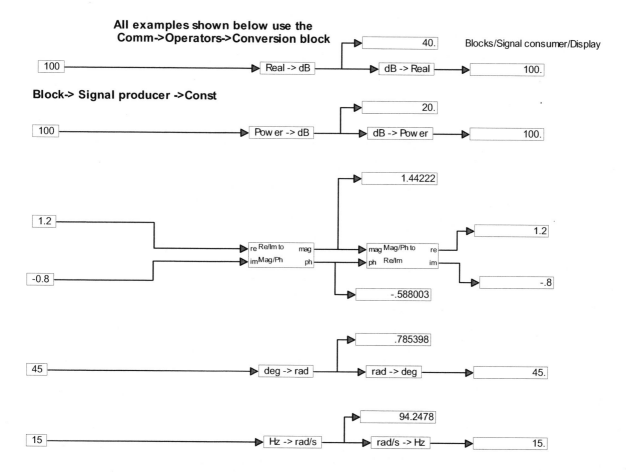

All examples shown below use the
Comm->Operators->Conversion block

Blocks/Signal consumer/Display

| 100 |────────────────────────▶| Real -> dB |─────┬───▶| 40. |
                                                    └───▶| dB -> Real |───▶| 100. |

Block-> Signal producer ->Const

| 100 |────────────────────────▶| Pow er -> dB |─────┬───▶| 20. |
                                                      └───▶| dB -> Pow er |───▶| 100. |

| 1.2 |
| -0.8 |
re Re/Im to   mag   mag Mag/Ph to   re   1.44222 / 1.2
im Mag/Ph   ph   ph Re/Im   im   -.588003 / -.8

| 45 |────────────────────────▶| deg -> rad |─────┬───▶| .785398 |
                                                  └───▶| rad -> deg |───▶| 45. |

| 15 |────────────────────────▶| Hz -> rad/s |─────┬───▶| 94.2478 |
                                                   └───▶| rad/s -> Hz |───▶| 15. |

3. Explain the system, and write your conclusion by using a label (Blocks > Annotation > Blocks) inside the figure.

4. Check the operation of the conversion block by using different numbers in the input, and change the background color of the display to red.

5. Print a copy for your instructor.

Exercise 6

Objective

To convert bits into symbol and vise versa

Lab Setup

Standard lab setup with VisSim installed

Procedure

1. Simulate the following system using the following blocks

   a) **Bits to symbol block**: Comm > Digital > Bits to symbol

   This block accepts inputs from n parallel binary bit streams and outputs the corresponding symbol number. You can specify the number of input data streams. The mapping is simply the decimal equivalent of the binary number formed by combining the input bit streams. Rounding is performed on the input data. Any value $x > 0.5$ is considered a 1; a lesser value is considered a 0.

   Bit Order:

   LSB First: Indicates that x1 is considered the least significant bit

   MSB First: Indicates that x1 is considered the most significant bit

   Number of Input Bits:

   Indicates the number n of incoming binary data streams valid range is 2 to 16.

   b) **Const:** Block > Signal producer > const

   c) **Symbols to bits**: Comm > Digital > Symbols to bits

   Number of Output Bits:

   Indicates the number n output binary data stream, valid range is 2 to 16.

   d) **Display**: Block >Signal consumer > Display

   d) **Simulation properties**:

   System > System properties

   Frequency: 100

   End: 10

Block->Signal consumer-> Display

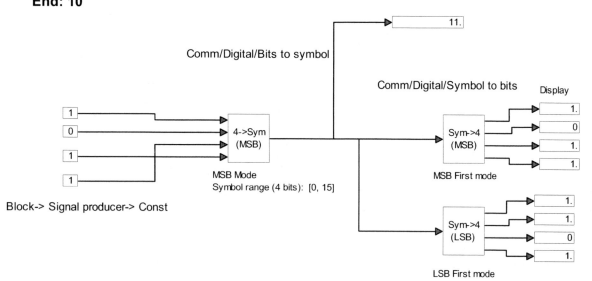

Comm/Digital/Bits to symbol

Comm/Digital/Symbol to bits

Display

4->Sym (MSB)

MSB Mode
Symbol range (4 bits): [0, 15]

Sym->4 (MSB)

MSB First mode

Sym->4 (LSB)

LSB First mode

Block-> Signal producer-> Const

2. Explain the system, and write your conclusion by using a label inside the figure.

3. Check the operation of the bits to symbol block by using different numbers in the input, and change the background color of the display to blue.

4. Print a copy for your instructor.

Exercise 7

Objective

To learn the function of sin and sign

Lab Setup

Standard lab setup with VisSim installed

Procedure

1. Simulate the following system using the following blocks

   a) Sin:

   Block > Transcendental > Sin

   The sin block produces the sine function of the input signal. The input signal is represented in radians.

   b) Sign:

   Block > Arithmetic > Sign

   The sign block determines the sign of the scalar input signal. The sign block outputs +1 when the input is greater than zero, -1 when the input is less than zero, and 0 when the input is zero.

   c) Ramp function:

   Block > Signal producer > Ramp function

   d) Simulation properties:

   System > System properties

   Frequency: 100

   End: 10

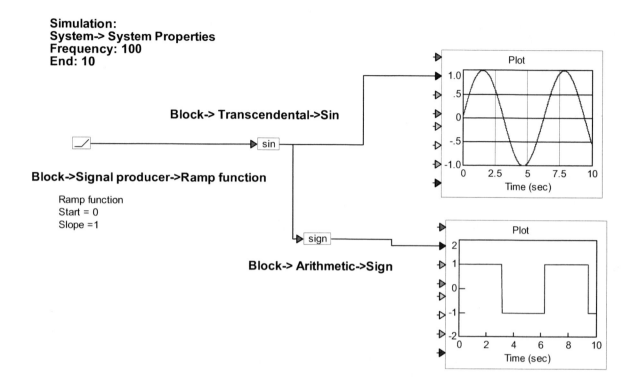

Simulation:
System-> System Properties
Frequency: 100
End: 10

Block-> Transcendental->Sin

Block->Signal producer->Ramp function

Ramp function
Start = 0
Slope =1

Block-> Arithmetic->Sign

2. Explain the operation of the system, and write your conclusion by using a label on your plot.

3. Print a copy for your instructor.

Exercise 8

Objective

To show function of the polynomial block and XY plot

Lab Setup

Standard lab setup with VisSim installed

Polynomial block

Block Category: Comm > Operators > Polynomial

This block computes g(x) for g(x) up to a fifth order polynomial.

x = Input signal

y = Output signal g(x)

$$g(x) = aX^5 + bX^4 + cX^3 + dX^2 + eX^1 + fX^0$$

Show Formula displays the polynomial formula as part of the block's name.

Decimal Digits specifies the number of decimal digits to use for the polynomial coefficients in the displayed block name (if the **Show Formula** check box is selected).

Procedure

1. Simulate the following system using the following blocks

   a) Polynomial: Comm > Operators > Polynomial.

   Click on the polynomial block and set the coefficient of the polynomial function in the dialog box.

   Set the number of decimal digit to 2

   For the case of showing the formula check the box

   b) Plot: Block > Signal consumer > Plot or choose the one from the tool part button

   Settings:

   Options

   -Fixed bound

   -XY Plot (X-axis is chosen as input 1.)

-Grid line

Axis

-Y upper	20	-Timing Scale	Millisecond
-Y lower	-40		
-X upper	6		
-X lower	-4		

Label

-Title:	Plot functions (XY Plot)
-X label	Time (sec)
-Y label	Y(x)

c) **Ramp function**: Block > Signal producer > ramp function
Set time delay (sec) = 0
Set slope =1

d) **Const block**: Block > Signal producer > Const
Set value = -4

e) **Summing junction**: Block > Arithmetic > Summing junction

f) **Simulate**:
System > System Properties.
Range

-Frequency	100
-End	10

The rest are set by default.

Simulation:
System > System properties
Frequency : 100
End: 10

x range is [-4, 6]

Block->Signal producer->
Ramp function

Ramp function
Start = 0
Slope =1

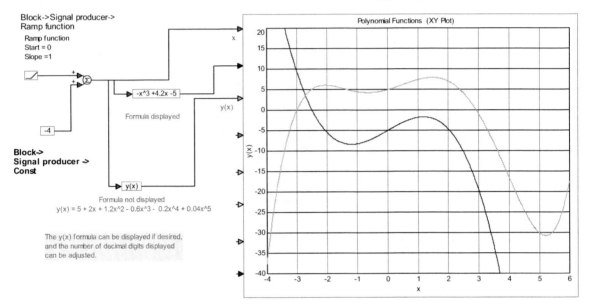

-x^3 +4.2x -5

Formula displayed

y(x)

-4

Block->
Signal producer ->
Const

y(x)

Formula not displayed
y(x) = 5 + 2x + 1.2x^2 - 0.6x^3 - 0.2x^4 + 0.04x^5

The y(x) formula can be displayed if desired,
and the number of decimal digits displayed
can be adjusted.

Polynomial Functions (XY Plot)

2. Explain the operation of the system, and write your conclusion by using a label.

3. Print a copy for your instructor.

Exercise 9

Objective

As an exercise demonstrate the operation of XY plotting

Lab Setup

Standard lab setup with VisSim installed

Procedure

1. Find all the boxes and the setting of all units to simulate the following figure.
2. Write down your observation and conclusion. Prepare a copy of the result for your instructor.

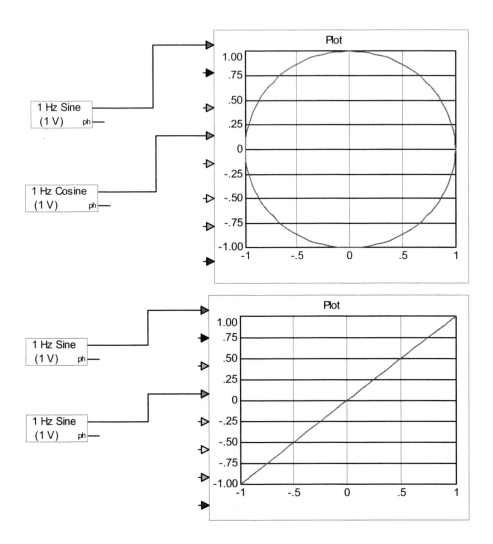

Exercise 10

Objective

To demonstrate the operation of the gain block and average power measurement

Lab Setup

Standard lab setup with VisSim installed

Gain Block

Block Category: Comm > Operators > Gain

The gain block can be used to specify either a gain or a loss in dB

This block lets you specify a gain value in decibels. This value may be positive or negative.

Average Power Operator

Block Category: Comm > Estimators > Average power (real)

This block estimates the Average [Complex] Power of the input [complex] signal. Two versions of this block exist: one for Complex signals and one for Real signal. Two power estimation modes are available: running window and sliding window. The two modes are described in more detail below.

$x1$ = Input signal ([Re, Im] for Complex)

$x2$ = Reset signal (resets when $x2 > 1$)

y = Power estimate

Load:

1 Ohm

   Specifies a load resistance of 1 Ohm

50 Ohms

   Specifies a load resistance of 50 Ohms

Output Units

dBm

   Average power is specified in dBm.

Watts

   Average power is specified in watts.

dBW

Average power is specified in dBW.

Mode

Running

Specifies that the average power estimate is computed using all simulation samples since the last reset pulse or simulation start. The reset signal is optional.

Sliding

Specifies that the average power estimate is computed over a sliding window

Window Size

This specifies the size of the sliding window averaging buffer in simulation steps. This parameter is available only when in Sliding mode.

Initial Value

Specifies the initial value stored in the sliding window buffer at simulation start. This parameter is available only when in Sliding mode.

Procedure

1. Simulate the following system using the following block in VisSim.

   a) **Sine**: Comm > Signal sources > Sinusoid

   b) **Gain**: Comm > Operators > Gain

   c) **Av. Power**: Comm > Estimators > Av. Power

   d) **Display**: Blocks > Signal consumer > Display

   e) **Plot**: Use toolbar button

   f) **Simulate**:
   System > System Properties.
   Range
   -Frequency   100
   -End   3

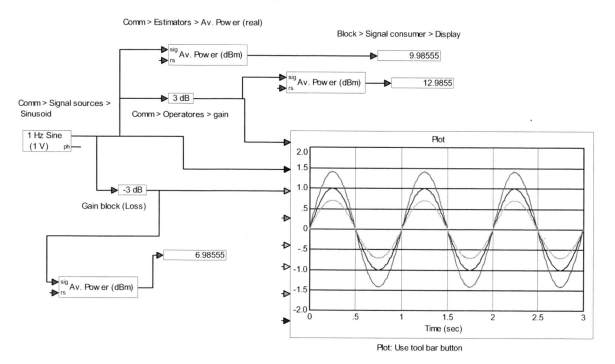

Simulation:
System > System properties
Frequency: 100
End: 3

Comm > Estimators > Av. Power (real)

Block > Signal consumer > Display

sig
Av. Power (dBm)
rs

9.98555

sig
Av. Power (dBm)
rs

12.9855

Comm > Signal sources >
Sinusoid

3 dB

Comm > Operatores > gain

1 Hz Sine
(1 V)   ph

Plot

-3 dB

Gain block (Loss)

6.98555

sig
Av. Power (dBm)
rs

Plot: Use tool bar button

2. Change the amplitude of the input sine to 2 volts and run the simulation. Calculate power in dBm for 50 ohm resistor and check your calculation versus simulated output in display box. Justify your results. Write your justification by using a label .

3. Print a copy for your instructor.

Lab 2: Signals, Amplification (Gain), Noise, Complex Math, and Random Signal Generation

Exercise 1

Objective

To learn how to add multiple signal sources to simulate voice signal

Lab Setup

Standard lab setup with VisSim installed

Introduction

A voice signal can be considered a combination of different sinusoidal signals with different amplitudes and frequencies. Typical speech signals seldom distribute uniformly across the entire voice-band spectrum (300 Hz to 3300 Hz). Instead, the spectral power of most speech energy concentrates at three or four peak frequencies called formants.

Summing Junction

Block Category: Block > Arithmetic > Summing junction

The Summing Junction block produces the sum of two signed input signals. You can toggle the sign of the input signals (switch from positive to negative and vice versa) by holding down the CTRL key and clicking the right mouse button over the connector tab.

You can add or remove input from the summing junction.

To add/remove connector tabs:

a) From the toolbar, choose $\rightarrow^+$ (for adding) or $\rightarrow^-$ (for deleting)

Do one of the following:

To	Do this
Add a connector tab	Point to where you want the tab. The short black line indicates tab placement. Click the mouse.
Delete a connector tab	Point to the tab to be deleted. The selected tab has a short black line over it. Click the mouse.

b) Repeat the above steps for as many tabs as you want to add or delete.

c) Click the mouse on empty screen space to exit this command.

Procedure

1. Simulate the following system using VisSim. Four sinusoidal signals with different frequencies and amplitudes are added together by a summing junction.

+

Simulation:
System> System properties
Frequency: 10000
End: 0.01

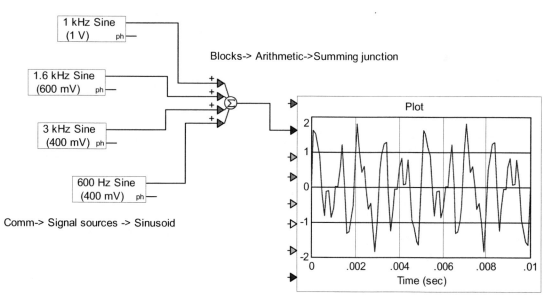

Simulation Properties for this Exercise

Click on System > System Properties

a) Range

-Frequency	10,000
-End	0.01

The rest are set by default.

2. Change the frequencies of the sine waves and note the effects on the display.

   Notice that the simulation frequency is 10,000 since the input frequencies are in KHz range.

3. Write your conclusion on your simulation using a label box, located in Block > Annotation> label. Print a copy of your simulation for your instructor.

Exercise 2

Objective

To show the effect of amplification and added noise on the simulated voice signal

Lab Setup

Standard lab setup with VisSim installed

Introduction

Noise can be any kind of undesired signal incorporated with the original signal. When noise signals become comparable with the analog input signal, they affect the performance of the analog communication system. All the amplifiers have some inherent noise of their own to contribute to the signal being processed in analog communication receivers. High quality amplifiers are designed to have an output signal to noise ratio as close as possible to the input signal to noise ratio.

Noise Block

Block Category: Comm > Signal Sources > Noise

This block generates Gaussian random noise according to the specified noise density or noise temperature parameter. Uniform noise at the level specified is generated over the entire [-fs/2, +fs/2] range. The simulation sampling frequency (fs) is automatically taken into account when the noise is generated. The block supports both 1 Ohm and 50 Ohms load impedances.

Noise Units:

dBm/Hz : Noise density is specified in dBm/Hz.

Watts/Hz: Noise density is specified in watts/Hz.

Degrees Kelvin:

Setting the equivalent noise temperature in degrees Kelvin specifies noise density.

Noise Density (Noise Temperature):

Specifies the source's noise density (noise temperature) in either watts/Hz, dBm/Hz, or degrees Kelvin depending on the Noise Units setting

Procedure

1. Simulate the following system using VisSim. Use the following blocks:

   a) **Sine**: Comm > Signal sources > Sinusoid

   b) **Summing junction**: Block > Arithmetic > Summing junction

      Add more input to that. See lab 2 Exercise 1.

   c) **Gain**: Block Category: Comm > Operators Gain

      This block lets you specify a gain value in decibels. This value may be positive or negative.

      Settings

      Load: 50 ohm

      Noise unit: W/Hz

      Gain: 3dB

   d) **Noise**: Comm > Signal Sources > Noise

      Settings

      Load: 50

      Noise unit: W/Hz

      Noise density: 5e-4

   e) Plot: Use toolbar button

   f) **Simulation Properties for this Exercise**

      Click on System > System properties

Range	
Frequency	10,000
End	0.01

      The rest are set by default.

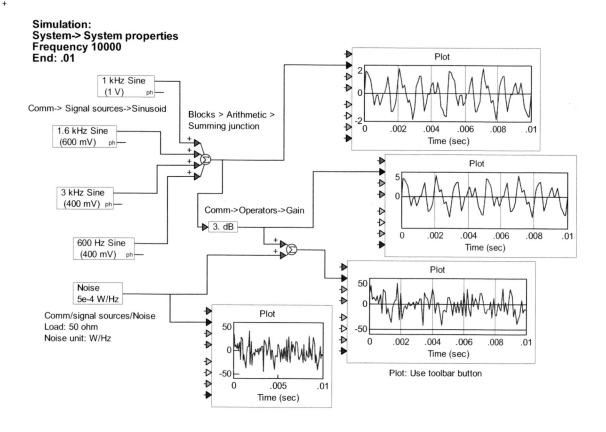

Simulation:
System-> System properties
Frequency 10000
End: .01

1 kHz Sine
(1 V)   ph

Comm-> Signal sources->Sinusoid

1.6 kHz Sine
(600 mV)   ph

3 kHz Sine
(400 mV)   ph

600 Hz Sine
(400 mV)   ph

Noise
5e-4 W/Hz

Comm/signal sources/Noise
Load: 50 ohm
Noise unit: W/Hz

Blocks > Arithmetic >
Summing junction

Comm->Operators->Gain

3. dB

Plot

Plot

Plot

Plot

Plot: Use toolbar button

2. Change the amount of noise in the noise block and observe the effect on the output signal.

3. Write your conclusion on your simulation using a label box, located in Blocks > Annotation > label. Print a copy of your simulation for your instructor.

Exercise 3

Objective

To show the operation of the frequency sweep block

Lab Setup

Standard lab setup with VisSim installed

Introduction

This unit is useful in studying cases that involve input signals that change in a range of frequencies. Once the sweep is completed, the sweep resumes at the start frequency and specified start phase. A phase discontinuity will usually take place at this point.

Procedure

1. Simulate the following system using the following blocks

    a) **Frequency Sweep** : Comm > Signal Sources > Frequency sweep

        Sweep parameters:

        Start freq= 1KHz

        Stop freq= 10Khz

        Sweep interval = 5m sec

        Amplitude = 1V

    b) **Plot:** Use toolbar button

        Fixed bounds

        Axis:

        Y upper: 3

        Y lower: -3

        X upper: 10

        X lower: 0

    c) **Simulation Properties for this Exercise**

        Click on System > System properties

        Range

        Frequency   100,000

        End   0.01

Simulation:
System-> System properties
frequency: 100000
End: 0.01

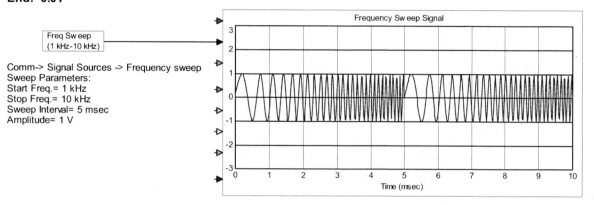

Freq Sweep
(1 kHz-10 kHz)

Comm-> Signal Sources -> Frequency sweep
Sweep Parameters:
Start Freq.= 1 kHz
Stop Freq.= 10 kHz
Sweep Interval= 5 msec
Amplitude= 1 V

Notes:
Once the sweep interval is completed, the sweep resumes
at the start frequency and specified start phase. A phase
discontinuity will usually take place at this point.

Plot: Use Toolbar button
Click Fixed Bound
Y Upper bound= 3
Y lower bound = -3
X upper bound = 10
X lower bound = 0

2. Change the sweep rate, start frequency, and stop frequency. Observe the plot.

3. Write your conclusion on your simulation using a label box, located in Block
    Blocks > Annotation > label. Print a copy of your simulation for your instructor.

Exercise 4

Objective

To show the operation of the Random Symbol generation

Lab Setup

Standard lab setup with VisSim installed

Introduction

This exercise is useful in simulating cases that involve input symbols that change randomly with time.

Random Symbol

Block Category: Comm > Signal Sources > Random symbol

This block generates uniformly distributed random symbols (integer values) between 0 and N-1, where N is the number of total symbols. The value of N, the symbol rate, and an initial delay can be specified. This block can also accept an external clock. A clock value greater than 0.5 is considered high.

Number of Symbols:

Specifies the number of different output symbols N. The output values will range between 0 and N-1.

Timing:

Internal: Indicates internal clock timing. The symbol rate and delay need to be specified.

External: Indicates external timing. An external clock must be provided at the x1 input.

Symbol Rate:

Specifies the data sequence symbol rate in symbols/second. This parameter is only available in Internal Timing mode.

Start Time:

Specifies the starting time, in seconds, for the output sequence. This parameter is only available in Internal Timing mode.

Procedure

1. Simulate the following system using the following blocks.

    a) **Random symbol**: Comm > Signal sources > Random Symbol

    > Settings:
    >
    > Symbol rate = 5 Hz
    >
    > Timing: Internal
    >
    > Number of symbols: 4

    b) **Polynomial** : Comm > operators > Polynomial

    > Polynomial block also can be used to add or subtract a number from the input to separate two signals in the plot. See also lab #1 Exercise 2.
    >
    > Here -2 units are subtracted from the clock output and clock shows two units bellow the symbols in the plot.
    >
    > The coefficients of the polynomial (x-2) are:
    >
    > X^0 = -2
    >
    > X^1 = 1
    >
    > Other coefficient = 0
    >
    > Click on Show formula and set Decimal digit to 2

    c) **Plot**: Use toolbar button

    > Fixed bound
    >
    > Axis for top plot
    >
    > Y upper: 4
    >
    > Y lower: -3
    >
    > X upper: 10
    >
    > X lower: 0
    >
    > For the lower plot see the figure

    d) **Simulation Properties for this Exercise**

    > Click on System > System properties
    >
    > Range
    >
    > Frequency   100
    >
    > End   10
    >
    > The rest are set by default.

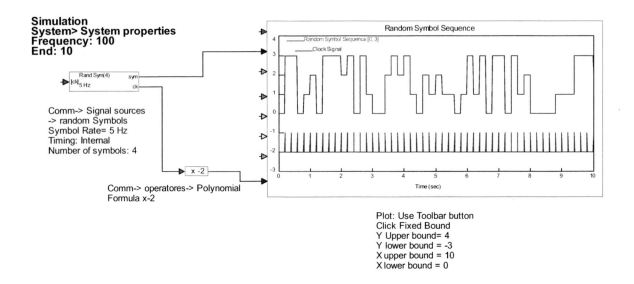

Simulation
System> System properties
Frequency: 100
End: 10

Rand Sym(4)   sym
[ck] 5 Hz   ck

Comm-> Signal sources
-> random Symbols
Symbol Rate= 5 Hz
Timing: Internal
Number of symbols: 4

x -2

Comm-> operatores-> Polynomial
Formula x-2

Plot: Use Toolbar button
Click Fixed Bound
Y Upper bound= 4
Y lower bound = -3
X upper bound = 10
X lower bound = 0

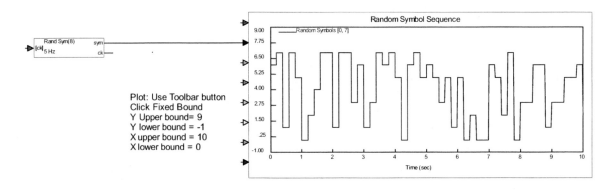

Rand Sym(8)   sym
[ck] 5 Hz   ck

Plot: Use Toolbar button
Click Fixed Bound
Y Upper bound= 9
Y lower bound = -1
X upper bound = 10
X lower bound = 0

2. Generate a random symbol with 16 symbols, a symbol rate of 10 Hz, and a start time of .1 sec.

3. Write your conclusion on your simulation using a label box, located in Block Blocks > Annotation > label. Print a copy of your simulation for your instructor.

Exercise 5

Objective

To show the operation of the Pseduo Noise (PN) sequence generation

Lab Setup

Standard lab setup with VisSim installed

Introduction

PN sequence is useful in simulating cases that involve an input sequence that changes randomly with time.

PN sequence

Block Category: Comm > Signal Sources > PN sequence

This block generates a maximum length pseudo noise (PN) sequence, also known as a pseudo random binary sequence (PRBS). The generator shift register size, generator polynomial, initial state, and bit rate can be specified. The block can also accept an external clock.

The output sequence can be augmented with an extra zero.

Example:

n = 7   PN length = 127   Generator coefficient = 211 octal (10001001)

Shift Register Size:

Specifies the order n of the PN sequence and determines its length. The sequence length is $2n - 1$ ($2n$ for augmented sequences), where n is the shift register size. Valid range is from 2 to 28.

Sequence Offset:

Determines the starting position of the PN sequence. The offset value is used to advance the shift register from its known starting point state. Valid range is from 0 to $2n - 1$, or 32767.

Initial State:

Specifies the initial state of the internal shift register in octal format. The least significant bit (LSB) represents the initial output; the remaining bits represent the next n-1 outputs. For example, 56 octal are 101110.

Generator Coefficient:

Specifies the generator code for the PN sequence in octal format. The default code for a given order n can be obtained by selecting the Default Generator Coefficient option. Note that this value is always odd.

Zero Augmented Sequence:

Instructs the PN generator to augment the output sequence with an extra zero. The extra zero is inserted after n-1 consecutive zeros is encountered in the output sequence.

Use Default Generator Coefficient:

Loads the default generator coefficient for each order n. The default code represents the minimal weight primitive polynomial.

Output Mode:

Bi-level: Indicates that the signal amplitudes associated with output the sequence is {-1, 1}

Binary: Indicates that the signal amplitudes associated with output the sequence is {0, 1}

Timing:

Internal: Indicates internal clock timing. The bit rate and start time need to be specified.

External: Indicates external timing. An external clock must be provided at the x1 input.

Bit Rate:

Specifies the PN sequence bit rate in bits per second. This parameter is only available in Internal Timing mode.

Start Time:

Specifies a start time, in seconds, for the PN sequence. This parameter is only available in Internal Timing mode.

Procedure

1. Simulate the following system using the following blocks.

a) **Pseudo Noise (PN)**: Comm > Signal sources > PN sequence

Settings for the top PN sequence:

Bit rate = 5 bps

Shift register size = 7

Initial state= 37

Binary : 0,1

Timing: Internal

Use default generator coefficient

For the other PN sequence settings see the following Figure

b) **Polynomial** : Comm > operators > Polynomial

Polynomial block also can be used to add or subtract a number from the input to separate two signals in the plot. See also lab #1 Exercise 2.

Here -2 units are subtracted from the clock output and clock shows two units bellow the symbols in the plot.

The coefficients of the polynomial (x-2) are:

$X^0 = -2$

$X^1 = 1$

Other coefficient = 0

Click on Show formula

Decimal digit to 2

c) **Plot**: Use toolbar button

Fixed bound

Axis

Y upper: 2

Y lower: -3

X upper: 6

X lower: 0

d) Simulation Properties for this Exercise

Click on System > System properties

Range

Frequency   100

End   6

Simulation:
System > System properties
Frequency: 100
End: 6

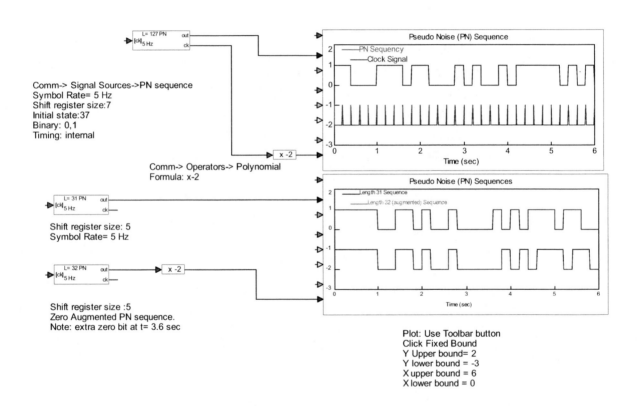

Comm-> Signal Sources->PN sequence
Symbol Rate= 5 Hz
Shift register size:7
Initial state:37
Binary: 0,1
Timing: internal

Comm-> Operators-> Polynomial
Formula: x-2

Shift register size: 5
Symbol Rate= 5 Hz

Shift register size :5
Zero Augmented PN sequence.
Note: extra zero bit at t= 3.6 sec

Plot: Use Toolbar button
Click Fixed Bound
Y Upper bound= 2
Y lower bound = -3
X upper bound = 6
X lower bound = 0

2. Generate a 255 bi-level PN sequence with a bit rate of 10 .

3. Write your conclusion on your simulation using a label box, located in Block > Annotation > label. Print a copy of your simulation for your instructor.

Exercise 6

Objective

To generate symbol number from n parallel binary bit stream

Lab Setup

Standard lab setup with VisSim installed

Introduction

This exercise is useful in simulating cases that involve input of a series of parallel binary sequences that change randomly with time. The output is the conversion of these binary numbers to equivalent symbols level. This is similar to digital to analog conversion

Bits to Symbol

Block Category: Comm > Digital > Bits to symbol

This block accepts inputs from n parallel binary bit streams and outputs the corresponding symbol number. You can specify the number of input data streams. The mapping is simply the decimal equivalent of the binary number formed by combining the input bit streams. Rounding is performed on the input data. Any value $x > 0.5$ is considered a 1; any lesser value is considered a 0.

Bit Order:

LSB First: Indicates that x1 is considered the least significant bit

MSB First: Indicates that x1 is considered the most significant bit

Number of Input Bits:

Indicates the number n of incoming binary data streams. Valid range is 2 to 16.

Procedure

1. Simulate the following system using the following blocks

a) **Bit to symbol**: Comm > Digital > Bits to symbol

> Settings:
>
> Click MSB First
>
> Number of input bits = 3

b) **Pseudo Noise (PN)**: Comm > Signal sources > PN sequence

> Settings for the top PN sequence:
>
> Bit rate = 5 bps
>
> Shift register size =13
>
> Initial state= 37
>
> Output Mode: Binary : 0,1
>
> Timing: Internal
>
> Use default generator coefficient
>
> For the other PN sequence settings see the following Figure

c) **Plot**: Use toolbar button

> Fixed bound
>
> Axis
>
> Y upper: 8
>
> Y lower: -1
>
> X upper: 10
>
> X lower: 0

d) **Simulation Properties for this Exercise**

> Click on System > System properties
>
> Range
>
> Frequency   100
>
> End   10
>
> The rest are set by default.

Simulation:
System> System properties
Frequency:100
End:10

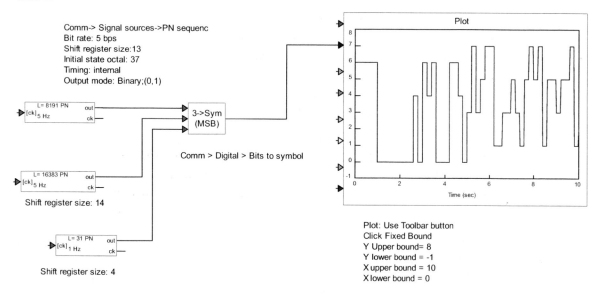

Comm-> Signal sources->PN sequenc
Bit rate: 5 bps
Shift register size:13
Initial state octal: 37
Timing: internal
Output mode: Binary;(0,1)

L= 8191 PN   out
[ck] 5 Hz   ck

3->Sym
(MSB)

Comm > Digital > Bits to symbol

L= 16383 PN   out
[ck] 5 Hz   ck

Shift register size: 14

L= 31 PN   out
[ck] 1 Hz   ck

Shift register size: 4

Plot: Use Toolbar button
Click Fixed Bound
Y Upper bound= 8
Y lower bound = -1
X upper bound = 10
X lower bound = 0

2. Change the bit orders to LSB, and explain the effect

3. Add one more input, and study the output

4. Write your conclusion on your simulation using a label box, located in Block > Annotation >label. Print a copy of your simulation for your instructor.

Exercise 7

Objective

To demonstrate the usage of the complex math operation of VisSim

Lab Setup

Standard lab setup with VisSim installed

Introduction

Complex number math operation is an important part of most communication system simulation. In this unit, operation of all the blocks in complex math will be studied.

Procedure

1. Simulate the following system using the following blocks
   a) **Complex math**: Comm > complex math

      Choose proper boxes for addition, Subtraction, Multiplication and division
   b) **Cont:** Blocks > Signal producer > const
   c) **Negation**: Blocks > Arithmetic > -x

      This block negate the input for performing the subtraction
   d) **Display**: Block > Signal consumer > Display
   e) **Simulation Properties for this Exercise**

      Click on System > System properties

      Range

      -Frequency   100

      -End   10

      The rest are set by default.

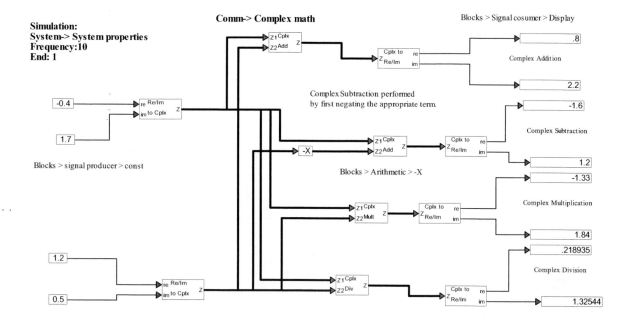

2. Check the operation of each unit with paper and pencil calculations.

3. Write your conclusion on your simulation using a label box, located in Block >Annotation > label. Print a copy of your simulation for your instructor.

Lab 3: Filters, Oscilloscope, and Communication Channels

Exercise 1

Objective

To demonstrate the operation of the Chebyshev filter and how to use the filter viewer

Lab Setup

Standard lab setup with VisSim installed

Introduction

Filters are one of the important blocks of any communication system. In this exercise, the operation of Chebychev filter and how to use the filter viewer will be studied.

Filters

Block Category: Comm > Filter > (IIR) Infinite Impulse Response

This block implements Infinite Impulse Response (IIR) filtering. It provides several well-known analog filter prototypes, such as Butterworth and Chebyshev designs, to choose from. This block accepts a real signal and outputs a real signal.

Filter Method

Indicates the filter design method to be used. Available methods are: Butterworth, Chebyshev Type I and Type II (Inverse Chebyshev), Bessel, and Elliptic

Filter Type

Indicates the desired filter type. Available types are: Low-pass, High-pass, Band-pass and Band-stop

Filter Order

Indicates the desired filter order. Valid range is from 1 to 20. Note that for the Band-pass and Band-stop types, the order must be even.

Cutoff Frequency 1

Specifies the desired cutoff frequency for the Low-pass and High-pass types as well as the lower cutoff frequency for the Band-pass and Band-stop types

Cutoff Frequency 2

Specifies the upper cutoff frequency for the Band-pass and Band-stop types

Pass-band Specification

Epsilon: Indicates that the filter response at the cutoff frequency is determined from the value of Epsilon. A value of 1 for Epsilon corresponds to an attenuation of 0.5 in power (3 dB point).

Ripple:

Indicates that the filter response at the cutoff frequency is determined from the value of Ripple. Ripple is a positive value, is expressed in dBs, and corresponds to the desired attenuation at the cutoff frequency.

Stop-band Attenuation:

Specifies the stop-band attenuation for the desired filter in dBs. This parameter is only applicable to Chebyshev Type II and Elliptic filters. Its value must exceed the Ripple value.

Units:

Hertz: Indicates that cutoff frequency values are in hertz

Radians/Sec: Indicates that cutoff frequency values are in radians/second

Show Coeff. :

Displays the polynomial coefficients of the IIR Filter's numerator and denominator in powers of z-1

Procedure

1. Simulate the following system using the following blocks:

   a) **Sine: Comm > Signal sources > Sinusoid**

   b) **Summing Junction: Blocks > Arithmetic > Summing junction**

   This block is used to add two different frequency sine signals

   c) **Filter: Comm > Filters > IIR**

   Settings:

   Filter method: Chebyshev

Cutoff Freq 1: 12

Units: Hertz

Filter order: 4

Filter type: Low pass

Ripple dB: 1

d) Plot: Use toolbar Button

Options: Fixed Bounds

Axis:

Y upper: 2

Y Lower: -2

X upper: 1

X lower: 0

e) Simulation:

System > System Properties

Frequency: 1000

End: 1

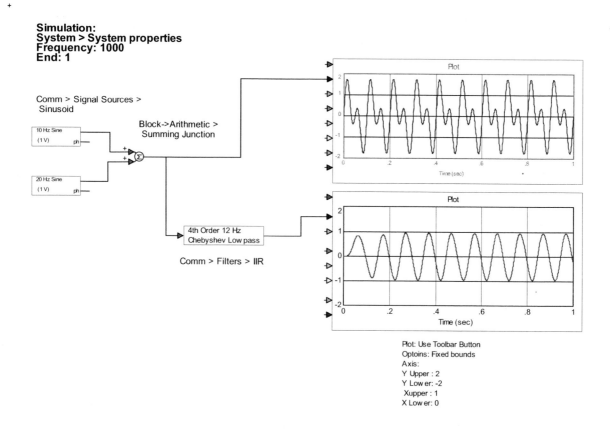

Simulation:
System > System properties
Frequency: 1000
End: 1

Comm > Signal Sources >
  Sinusoid

10 Hz Sine
(1 V)   ph

20 Hz Sine
(1 V)   ph

Block->Arithmetic >
Summing Junction

Plot

4th Order 12 Hz
Chebyshev Low pass

Comm > Filters > IIR

Plot

Plot: Use Toolbar Button
Optoins: Fixed bounds
Axis:
Y Upper : 2
Y Low er: -2
 Xupper : 1
X Low er: 0

2. Explain the difference between the input and output of the filter

3. To see the response of the filter, click over the filter block using the right mouse button, and press the "View response" button.

VisSim Comm response Viewer choices include:

Impulse response

Gain response (normal or dB)

Phase response

Group Delay response

For example the Gain response for this simulation is shown below, and you see that the cutoff frequency is around12 Hz.

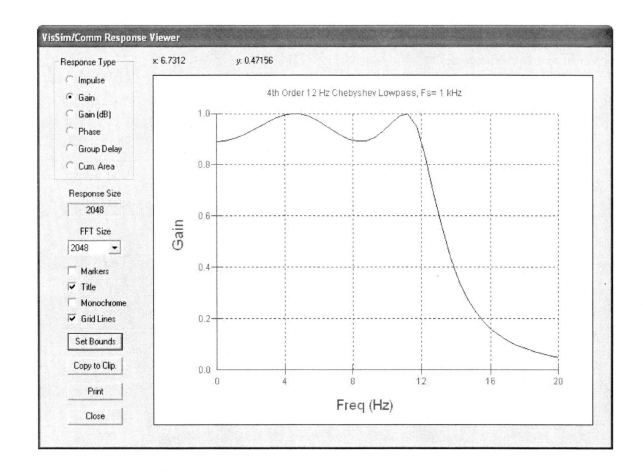

4. Choose the Gain response in dB and the Phase response. Print the result. Write down your conclusion as to how the gain and phase change versus the frequency.

5. Change the filter to high pass in order to separate the 20 Hz signal from 10 Hz and write down your conclusion.

6. Set up the following system and change the filter to band-pass. Write down your conclusion

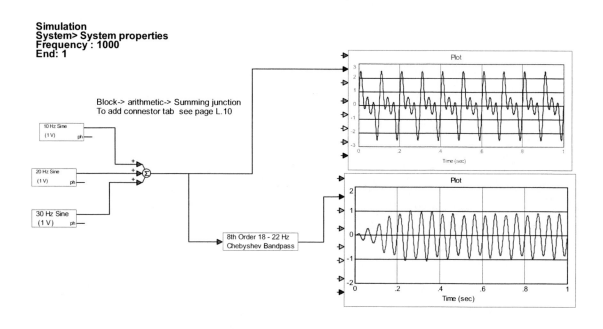

Simulation
System> System properties
Frequency : 1000
End: 1

Block-> arithmetic-> Summing junction
To add connestor tab see page L.10

10 Hz Sine
(1 V)   ph

20 Hz Sine
(1 V)   ph

30 Hz Sine
(1 V)   ph

8th Order 18 - 22 Hz
Chebyshev Bandpass

Exercise 2

Objective

To demonstrate the operation of Oscilloscope

Lab Setup

Standard lab setup with VisSim installed

Introduction

In this exercise two sinusoidal signals with different frequencies are multiplied together to generate a varying amplitude waveform. The output is demonstrated on channel A of the oscilloscope.

Oscilloscope Core

Block Category: Comm > Operators > oscilloscope (core)

This block emulates the use of a two input channel oscilloscope. The user can specify either input as the trigger source, specify falling or rising edge triggering, and set the trigger threshold level. The overall time span is also user defined. The output is viewed using a plot block configured in XY mode with an external trigger. An output trigger line, the A and B channel traces, and time axis outputs are provided for driving the plot block.

Once enabled by an external start pulse, the oscilloscope block monitors the input signal for a threshold crossing (i.e. a trigger event). Once triggered, it reads in N data points, where N is based on the desired time span, on both channels and then displays both traces all at once as a vector. Upon completing each trace, the block resets itself and waits for the next trigger event before repeating the above cycle.

Trigger Channel:

A Channel: Specifies Channel A is to be used for triggering the display

B Channel: Specifies Channel B is to be used for triggering the display

Triggering Mode:

Rising Edge: Forces the displayed trace to start, following a rising crossing of the specified threshold level

Level:

Falling Edge: Forces the displayed trace to start, following a falling crossing of the specified threshold level

Time Span: Specifies the desired time span (in seconds) for the display

Threshold: Specifies the voltage level (in volts) used for triggering the display

Plot Unit

Specify an XY plot:

In an XY plot, you can use one input signal to represent X coordinate generation. As time advances, the remaining input signals are plotted relative to the X-axis signal.

- Activate the XY Plot parameter.

- Under the X Axis parameter, choose the input signal to be used for X coordinate generation: 1 represents the input signal attached to the top input connector tab on the plot block, 2 represents the input signal attached to the second to the top input connector tab on the plot block, and so on.

- Click the OK button, or press ENTER.

Label the X-axis on an XY plot

In an XY plot, VisSim automatically labels the X-axis with the label for the input signal used for X coordinates generation. For example, if you activate XY Plot and choose 2 under X Axis, VisSim uses the label assigned to input signal 2.

- Click on the Labels tab.

- Enter a label for the input signal you chose to be used for X coordinates generation. The Trace 1 box corresponds to 1 in the X Axis parameter, the Trace 2 box corresponds to 2 in the X Axis parameter, and so on.

- Click the OK button, or press ENTER.

Fixed Bound

Specifies the region of the plot you want to view by letting you select the plotting bounds. When Fixed Bound is activated, VisSim uses the values for the X Upper Bound, X Lower Bound, Y Upper Bound, and Y Lower Bound parameters in the Axis property sheet.

External Trigger

Determines whether VisSim displays simulation data in the plot based on the value of an external trigger. When activated, External Trigger causes VisSim to place a round input connector on the plot block. When signal values entering the external trigger are

1, simulation data is plotted; when signal values entering the external trigger are 0, simulation data is not plotted. For example, the external trigger input for this simulation is 0 (the round input connector).

Read Coordinates

Overlays the plot with a set of crosshairs and displays crosshair position at the bottom of the plot. When you click the left or right mouse button, VisSim freezes the crosshairs. Click the left mouse button again to erase the crosshairs.

Maximum Plotted Point

Determines the smoothness and accuracy of a plot. The more data points you plot, the smoother and more accurate the plot. However, increasing the number of plotted data points also increases the time it takes to print and display the plot.

The maximum number of data points that can be plotted is 250 million.

If you know the maximum number of data points you want plotted in all your plots, you can set it as the default. See **Setting Simulation Defaults**.

Procedure

1. Simulate the following system using the following blocks:

   a) **Sine**; Comm > Signal sources > Sinusoid

   b) **Multiplier**: Blocks > Arithmetic > Multiplier

   c) **Impulse**: Comm > Signal sources > Impulse.

   d) **Divide by N**: Comm > Digital > Divide by N

   This block reduces display rate be N=10

   e) **Oscilloscope (core)**: Comm > Operators > Oscilloscope (core)
   Settings:

   Trigger Mode: Rising edge

   Trigger Channel: A

   Time span: 0.002

   Number of sweeps per update: 1

   Threshold (v): 0

   Trigger delay: 0

   f) **Plot:** Use Toolbar Button

   Plot properties: Options

   Fixed Bounds

External trigger: 0.

The external trigger is connected to the top input and considered input number 0.

XY Plot: X –axis: 4.

As you see the X axis shows time and time output is connected to number 4 input of the plot

Axis:

Y upper bound: 1.5

Y Lower bound: -1.5

X Upper bound: 0.002

X Lower bound: 0

Notice that a bubble is generated on the upper left corner of the input of the plot. This input is considered number zero and it is used for connecting the trigger pulse.

g) Simulation Properties for this Exercise

Click on System > System properties

Range

Frequency: 100,000

End :   2

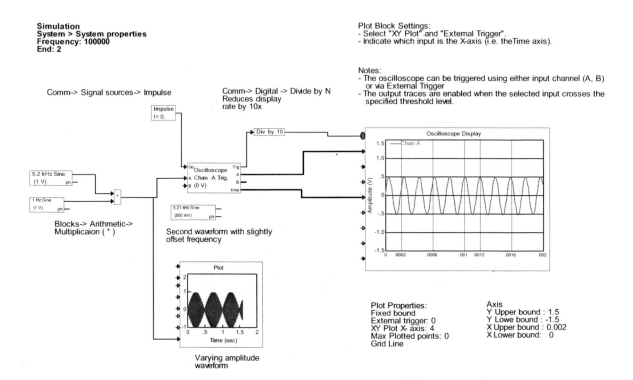

Simulation
System > System properties
Frequency: 100000
End: 2

Plot Block Settings:
- Select "XY Plot".and "External Trigger".
- Indicate which input is the X-axis (i.e. theTime axis).

Notes:
- The oscilloscope can be triggered using either input channel (A, B) or via External Trigger
- The output traces are enabled when the selected input crosses the specified threshold level.

Comm-> Signal sources-> Impulse

Comm-> Digital -> Divide by N
Reduces display
rate by 10x

Impulse
t= 0.

Div by 10

Oscilloscope Display

Chan A

5.2 kHz Sine
(1 V)   ph

Go Oscilloscope Trg
A Chan A Trig.
B (0 V)
time

1 Hz Sine
(1 V)   ph

Blocks-> Arithmetic->
Multiplicaion (*)

5.21 kHz Sine
(800 mV)   ph

Second waveform with slightly
offset frequency

Plot

Time (sec)

Varying amplitude
waveform

Plot Properties:
Fixed bound
External trigger: 0
XY Plot X- axis: 4
Max Plotted points: 0
Grid Line

Axis
Y Upper bound : 1.5
Y Lowe bound : -1.5
X Upper bound : 0.002
X Lower bound: 0

2. In the Properties dialog box of the plot, activate Read the Coordinate and Read the Values of the amplitude of the signal at various points.

3. In the Simulation Properties dialog window, click on the retrace enable, and write down what you observe in the plot.

4. Connect the second waveform with slightly offset frequency to channel B, and display both channel A and channel B. Print the result.

Exercise 3

Objective

To demonstrate the modeling of a channel by Additive White Gaussian Noise (AWGN)

Lab Setup

Standard lab setup with VisSim installed

Introduction

An AWGN is the most commonly used channel model for analyzing the performance of digital modulation techniques. It is regarded as the universal channel for digital communications. The channel is assumed to add white Gaussian noise to the signal traveling through it. White noise implies stationary with flat power spectral density. The noise is not frequency specific and so extends over infinite bandwidth. In this type of channel modeling, there is no amplitude loss, phase distortion or fading of the frequencies as the signal passes through the channel. AWGN is a model that is inherent in every channel.

In this exercise the effects of AWGN with different Signal-to-Noise ratios and different input signals are observed.

In order to avoid long wires and to make the diagram easy to read, the variable block (renamed "signal") is used to connect the units.

Variable

Block Category: Blocks > Annotation > Variable

The variable block is located under the Blocks menu in the Annotation category.

The variable block lets you name a signal and transmit it throughout your diagram without the use of wires. It is never a good idea to name a variable block -X or a number such as 1, or 2 or 3. In this exercise the name "Signal" is given to the variable.

To create a name for variable block

- Click the mouse over the variable block.
- The Set Variable Name dialog box appears. Type a name.

AWGN

Block Category: Comm < Channels >AWGN (real)

This block implements an Additive White Gaussian Noise (AWGN) channel in which Gaussian noise is added to the input signal. Two versions of this block exist: one Complex and one Real. The appropriate noise variance is automatically computed based on the simulation sampling frequency, specified noise bandwidth, and reference signal power. In the case of the complex version of the block, the two noise samples (real and imaginary) are independent. This block can also be used as a Source of Gaussian Noise by simply leaving the inputs disconnected or using a zero input.

Number of Runs: Specifies the number of simulation iterations (10 max.)

Equivalent Noise Bandwidth: Specifies the symbol rate R in hertz. This value is used internally to determine the energy per symbol as a fraction of the total specified signal power.

Ref. Power Units:

dBm in 50 Ohms: Indicates that the average power reference is specified as dBm into 50 Ohms impedance

Watts in 1 Ohm: Indicates that the average power reference is specified as watts into 1-Ohm impedance

Es/No: Specifies the symbol Signal-to-Noise Ratio in decibels for each run. E_b can be easily converted to Es by knowing the number of bits/symbol.

Procedure

1. Simulate the following system using the following blocks:

    a) **PN Sequence**: Comm > Signal sources > PN sequence

    Settings:

    Shift register size: 7

    Bit rate: 5

    Internal

    Binary (0, 1)

    b) **Variable**: Blocks < Annotation > variable

    Click on it and name it.

    c) **Const**: Block > Signal producer > Const

    d) **Summing junction**: Blocks > Arithmetic > Summing junction

    e) **AWGN** : Comm > Channels >AWGN (real)

Setting

E_s/N_0 (dB) = 25 and 30

Symbol Rate: 5 Hz

Ref Power units: Click dBm in 50 ohm

f) **Plot**: Use Toolbar Button

g) **Simulation Properties for this Exercise**

Click on System > System properties

Range

Frequency   100

End   10

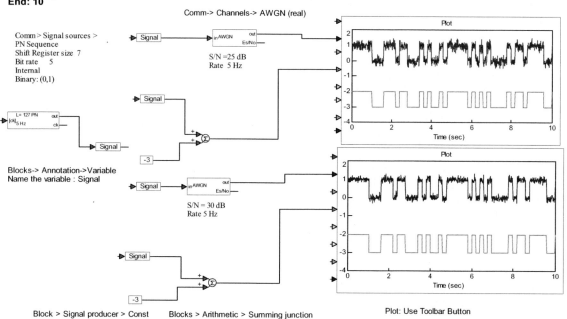

2. Write down your observation, What will happen on the noisy signal as E_b/N_0 decreases in AWGN unit.

3. Replace the PN sequence with Frequency sweep in Comm > Signal sources > Frequency sweep. Set the following parameters for the frequency sweep:

Start Frequency (Hz):   2

Stop Frequency (Hz):   10

Sweep duration: 5

Amplitude: 1

Run the simulation. This is an analog signal versus a digital PN sequence and it shows how noise will affect them. Write down your conclusion, and submit it to your instructor.

Exercise 4

Objective

1. To demonstrate the modeling of a channel by using Binary Symmetric Channel (BSC)
2. To study output error under different probability of error conditions

Lab Setup

Standard lab setup with VisSim installed

Introduction

The BSC has digital input and digital output. This is an ideal model for a discrete noisy channel. In this channel the probability that an input binary "0" is received as a binary "1" is the same as the probability that an input "1" is received as a binary "0." Similarly, the probability that the input bits are received correctly is equal for both binary input "0" and "1."

In this exercise, the effect of BSC with different values of probability of error is observed.

In order to avoid long wires and to make the diagram easy to read, variable blocks (renamed "signal" and "clock") are used to connect the units.

BSC

Block Category: Comm > Channels > Binary symmetric channel

This block implements a BSC. It expects a binary data stream {0, 1} and periodically flips the output bits according to the specified error probability. Any input value larger than 0.5 is considered a 1. This block takes a real signal as its input and outputs a real signal.

Channel Error Probability: Indicates the probability of a bit flip p. The range for this value is from 0.9999 to 3.1×10^{-8}.

Procedure

1. Simulate the following system using The following blocks:

a) **PN Sequence**: Comm > Signal sources > PN sequence

Settings:

Shift register size: 7

Bit rate: 5

Internal

Binary (0, 1)

b) **Variable**: Blocks < Annotation > variable

Click on it and name it. In this Exercise one variable is called Signal the other one is called clock

c) **Const**: Block > Signal producer > Const

d) **Summing junction**: Blocks > Arithmetic > Summing junction

e) **Binary symmetric channel**: Comm > Channels > Binary symmetric channel

Click on it and set it for different probability of error as shown on the diagram.

f) **Plot**: Use Toolbar Button

Fixed bounds

Axis:

Y upper bound: 2

Y lower bound: -2

X Upper bound: 10

X lower bound: 0

g) **Simulation Properties for this Exercise**

Click on System > System properties

Range

Frequency   100

End   10

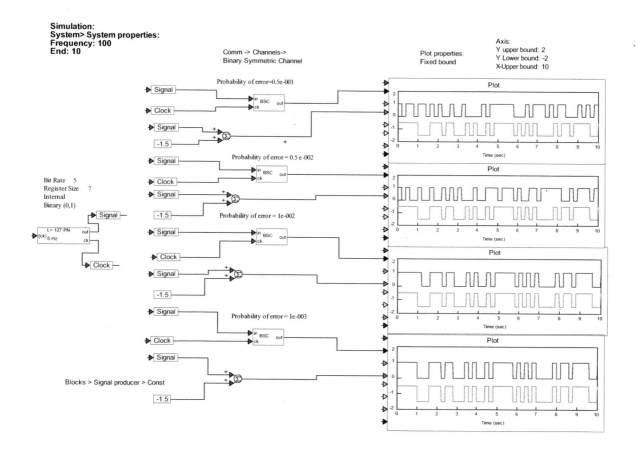

Simulation:
System> System properties:
Frequency: 100
End: 10

Comm -> Channels->
Binary Symmetric Channel

Plot properties:
Fixed bound

Axis:
Y upper bound: 2
Y Lower bound: -2
X-Upper bound: 10

Probability of error=0.5e-001

Probability of error = 0.5 e-002

Bit Rate   5
Register Size   7
Internal
Binary (0,1)

Probability of error = 1e-002

L = 127 PN

Probability of error = 1e-003

Blocks > Signal producer > Const

2. What happen as the probability of error increases? Write down your observation, and make a copy for your instructor.

Exercise 5

Objective

1. To demonstrate the modeling of a communication channel by using Multi-path channel unit.
2. Simulate multipath using delay and gain units

Lab Setup

Standard lab setup with VisSim installed

Introduction

Microwave line of sight, mobile and cellular channels are highly affected by fading and phase changes caused by the constant changes in the signal paths and reflections from obstructions. Fading is inherent in wireless radio channels, where there are multiple paths caused by reflection, refraction and, diffraction, which is the scattering of rays. The receiver antenna hence receives a composite signal, which is a combination of such multi-path signals.

In this exercise, the effect of multi-path signals are demonstrated using multi-path channel block.

Multi-path is equivalent to specifying multiple branches with varying weights and delays as shown in the following figure. Note that the branch delays are rounded to the closest available simulation steps.

Multi-path Channel Block

Block Category: Comm > Channels > Multipath

This block implements a Multi-path channel, in which multiple time- and phase-shifted versions of a signal are modeled as arriving simultaneously at a receiver. Multi-path channels are commonly used to model the interaction between a direct signal and multiple reflected path signals. The reflected signals affect both the amplitude and phase of the received signal. Block parameters include the number of total paths as well as the individual path's delay, relative gain, and phase rotation.

If the specified path delay is not an integer multiple of the simulation step size, the actual path delay implemented will correspond to the closest simulation step to the

---

desired delay value. This block takes a complex signal as its input and outputs a complex signal.

Number of Paths: Specifies the number of paths in the model. Up to four paths may be specified.

Initial Condition (Real): Specifies the Real component initial condition for the internal shift register used by the model

Initial Condition (Imag): Specifies the Imaginary component initial condition for the internal shift register used by the model

Delay Mode:

Sim Steps: Indicates the path delays are specified in simulation steps

Seconds: Indicates the path delays are specified in seconds

Path Delay: Specifies the delay in seconds or simulation steps associated with each path in the channel model

Weight: Specifies a relative weight for each of the model paths. This value is not in dB.

Phase Rotation: Specifies the phase rotation in degrees associated with each path

Gain Block

Block Category: Blocks > Arithmetic > Gain

The gain block multiplies the input signal by the gain amount. The input can be a scalar, vector, or matrix.

Delay Block

Block Category: Comm > Operators > Delay (real)

This block implements a multiple unit delay block. This block only operates on main simulation steps.

Delay: Specifies the delay in simulation steps or seconds depending on the selected Delay Mode. Valid range is from 1 to 32,767 steps.

Initial Condition: Indicates the block's output value for the first Delay simulation steps

Delay Mode:

Sim Steps: Indicates the delay size is specified in simulation steps

Seconds: Indicates the delay size is specified in seconds

Procedure

1. Simulate the following system using the following blocks.

a) **Sine:** Comm > Signal sources > Sinusoid

b) **Re/Im to complex**: Comm > Complex math < Re/Im to complex

c) **Cplx to real/Im**: Comm > Complex math > Cplx to Real/Im

d) **Gain**: Blocks > Arithmetic > gain

e) **Delay**: Comm > Operators > Delay (real)

f) **Summing junction**: Block > Arithmetic > Summing junction

   Add two more input to that. See Introduction: Getting Started page L 10

g) **Multi path**: Comm > Channels > Multipath

   Settings:

   Number of paths: 4

   Delay Mode: second

	Delay	Weight	Phase Rot
Path 1	04	.6	0
Path 2	7	.3	0
Path 3	2	.5	0
Path 4	0	.6	0

h) **Simulation Properties for this Exercise**

   Click on System > System properties

   Range

   -Frequency   20

   -End   2

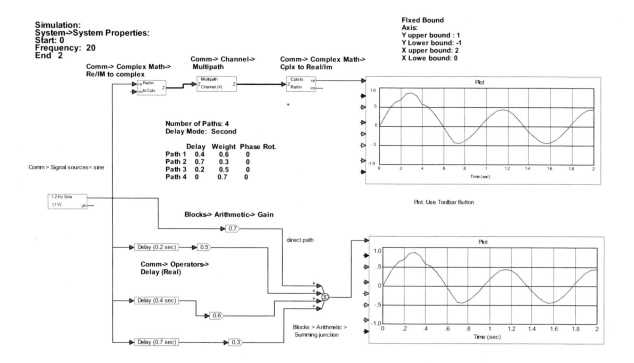

2. In this simulation you see the effect of multi-path in communication on signal transmission. A pure sine wave will change after passing through a multipath channel.

3. Write down your observation and make a copy for your instructor.

Lab 4: Spectrum Analyzer

Exercise 1

Objective

1. To learn how to use the spectrum analyzer block
2. Observe the frequency components of different waveform

Lab Setup

Standard lab setup with VisSim installed

Introduction

The history of the spectrum analyzer dates back to before World War II when radar and microwave communications were just beginning to evolve. There was a need to see on some type of display all the signals that might be present in a specific band of frequencies. In a spectrum analyzer a vertical line at the appropriate frequency can present each frequency component, and the length of the line can be drawn proportional to the magnitude at that frequency. This simple but effective plot makes it easy to see two things: the relative location of the frequencies and the relative amplitudes of the sinusoidal components. In this exercise, different waveforms are applied to the spectrum analyzer and their frequency components will be observed.

Spectrum Analyzer Block

Block Category: Comm > Operators >Spectrum (real)

This block outputs the complex Power Spectrum of the input signal. The spectrum can be continuously updated (once started by the external trigger) or produced at user-defined intervals (again, using the external trigger). Results are viewed using a plot block configured in XY mode with an external trigger. An output trigger line and x-axis output are provided for driving the plot block.

Two versions of this block exist: one Complex and one Real. The Real version of the block will only output the positive side of the spectrum (because it's mirror imaged) but. will include all signal energy, including that from the negative side of the spectrum.

The output spectrum can be in Watts, dBm, or dBm/Hz. When in dBm or dBm/Hz mode, the output is limited to −300 dBm.

Trigger Mode:

Continuous: Once a result has been output, the block immediately reads in more data.

Triggered: Once a result has been output, the block will wait for a new trigger before reading in new data.

FFT Window Type: Selects the desired window function to be used in computing the underlying FFT

Spectral Output:

Mag / Phase: Indicates that the result is represented by magnitude and phase component

Real / Imaginary: Indicates that the result is represented by real and imaginary components

FFT Size: Specifies the size N of the underlying FFT computation. Valid range is 8 to 16,384.

Unwrap Phase: Specifies that the computed phase output should be unwrapped. When not selected, the output phase is restricted to [-p, +p].

Remove Linear Phase: Specifies that linear phase, based on the provided delay input, should be removed from the phase output

Delay: Specifies the delay, in seconds, corresponding to the amount of linear phase to be removed from the phase result. This setting only applies when the Remove Linear Phase option is selected.

Number of FFT Averages: Specifies the number of consecutive power spectra (each of N points), which are averaged before producing the final result

Output Freq. Units: Specifies the frequency units for the x-axis drive signal (y4). Choices include hertz, kilohertz, megahertz, and gigahertz.

Power Spectrum Units:

Watts: The spectral output is represented in Watts.

dBm: The spectral output is represented in dBm. The output values represent total energy per bit.

dBm/Hz: The spectral output is represented as a power spectral density in dBm/Hertz.

Load

1 Ohm: The spectral output is referenced to a 1 Ohm load.

50 Ohms: The spectral output is referenced to a 50 Ohms load.

Procedure

1. Simulate the following system using the following blocks. In this simulation, the frequency setting in the simulation properties should be at least two times the source frequency you want to see.

   a) **Impulse**: Comm > Signal sources >Impulse

      Set t = 0.

   b) **Sine**: Comm > Signal sources > Sinusoid

      Settings:

      Frequency (Hz): 500

      Amplitude (V): 1

      Unit: Volt

      Phase output mode: Unwrapped

   c) **Rectangular pulse**: Comm > Signal sources > Rectangular pulses

      Settings
      Pulse Frequency (Hz): 1000

      High Level: 1

      Low level: -1

      Duty cycle (%): 50

      Start time (sec): 0

      Pulse Mode: Duty cycle

   d) **Triangular wave:** Comm > Signal sources > Waveform generator

      Click: Triangular wave

      Settings:

      Waveform frequency (Hz): 1000

      P.P Amplitude (V): 1

   e) **Saw tooth**: Comm > Signal sources > Waveform generator

      Click: Saw tooth

      Settings:

      Waveform frequency (Hz): 1000

      P.P Amplitude (V): 1

f) **Noise**: Comm > Signal sources > Noise

    Settings:

      Load: 50 ohm

      Noise unit: Degree Kelvin

      Noise temp (K): 290

g) **Spectrum (Real)** > Comm > operators > Spectrum (real)

    Settings;

    Trigger mode: Trigger

    Spectral output: Mag / Phase

    FFT window type: Rectangular

    FFT size: 512

    Power spectrum Units: Watts

    Load: 50 ohms

    Output frequency: Hz

h) **Plot:** Use Toolbar button

    Options:

    External Trigger: 0

    XY Plot: X axis: 4

    Grid lines

    Log Y

    Axis:

    Use figures to fix bounds and to set upper and lower bound.

    Notice that a bubble is generated on the upper left corner of the input of the plot. This input is considered number zero and it is used for connecting the trigger pulse.

i) **Simulation:**

System > System Properties

    Frequency: 2000 for the first one and 20000 for the rest

    End: 10

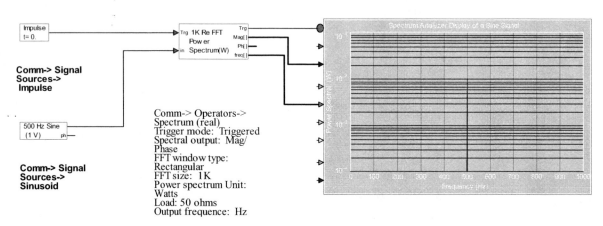

Simulation:
System-> System
properties
Frequency: 2000
End: 10

Plot
Properties:
External
trigger: 0
XY Plot X
axis: 4
Grid line
Log Y

Impulse
t= 0.

Comm-> Signal
Sources->
Impulse

Trg 1K Re FFT
Pow er
in Spectrum(W)

Trg
Mag[]
Ph[]
freq[]

500 Hz Sine
(1 V)   ph

Comm-> Operators->
Spectrum (real)
Trigger mode: Triggered
Spectral output: Mag/
Phase
FFT window type:
Rectangular
FFT size: 1K
Power spectrum Unit:
Watts
Load: 50 ohms
Output frequence: Hz

Comm-> Signal
Sources->
Sinusoid

2. Explain why at the frequency of 500 Hz only one line is shown on the plot. Print a copy of the result for your instructor.

3. Repeat part 2 by disconnecting the sine source and connecting a 1 KHz rectangular pulse source. Explain the difference in output spectrum. Remember that in this simulation, the frequency setting in the simulation properties should be at least two times the source frequency you want to see. In order to see the component more clearly, plot Y-axis as log.

4. Disconnect the rectangular source and connect the Triangle source and observe the spectrum.

5. Disconnect the triangle source and connect the Saw tooth source and observe the spectrum.

6. Disconnecting the saw tooth source and connect a noise source at 290 K and observe the spectrum.

7. Write your conclusion and make a copy of your results for your instructor.

Simulation:
System->System Properties:
Frequency: 20,000
End: 10

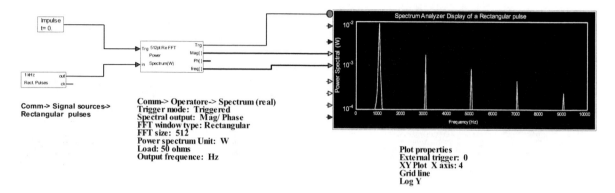

Comm-> Signal sources->
Rectangular pulses

Comm-> Operatore-> Spectrum (real)
Trigger mode: Triggered
Spectral output: Mag/ Phase
FFT window type: Rectangular
FFT size: 512
Power spectrum Unit: W
Load: 50 ohms
Output frequence: Hz

Plot properties
External trigger: 0
XY Plot X axis: 4
Grid line
Log Y

Simulation:
System-> System Properties:
Frequency: 20,000
End: 10

Comm-> Signal sources->
Impulse

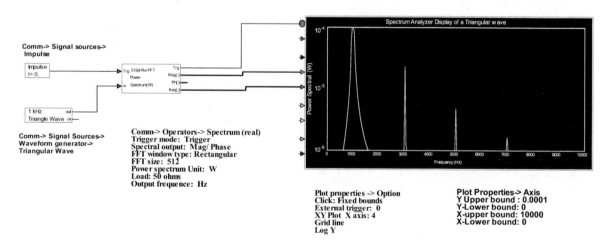

Comm-> Signal Sources->
Waveform generator->
Triangular Wave

Comm-> Operators-> Spectrum (real)
Trigger mode: Trigger
Spectral output: Mag/ Phase
FFT window type: Rectangular
FFT size: 512
Power spectrum Unit: W
Load: 50 ohms
Output frequence: Hz

Plot properties -> Option
Click: Fixed bounds
External trigger: 0
XY Plot X axis: 4
Grid line
Log Y

Plot Properties-> Axis
Y Upper bound : 0.0001
Y-Lower bound: 0
X-upper bound: 10000
X-Lower bound: 0

Simulation
System> SystemProperties:
Frequency: 20000
End: 10

Comm-> Signal sources->
Impulse

Impulse
t= 0.

1 kHz
Sawtooth Wave

Comm-> Signal Sources->
Waveform generator->
Sawtooth Wave

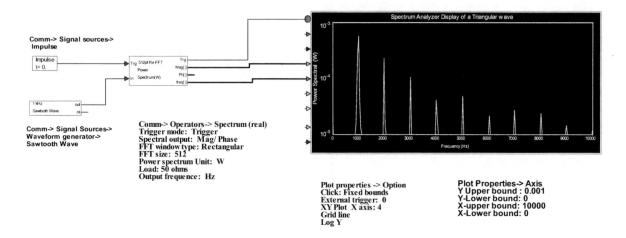

Comm-> Operators-> Spectrum (real)
Trigger mode: Trigger
Spectral output: Mag/ Phase
FFT window type: Rectangular
FFT size: 512
Power spectrum Unit: W
Load: 50 ohms
Output frequence: Hz

Plot properties -> Option
Click: Fixed bounds
External trigger: 0
XY Plot X axis: 4
Grid line
Log Y

Plot Properties-> Axis
Y Upper bound : 0.001
Y-Lower bound: 0
X-upper bound: 10000
X-Lower bound: 0

Simulation
System> System Properties:
Frequency: 20000
End: 10

Comm-> Signal sources->
Impulse

Impulse
t= 0.

Noise
290 K

Comm-> Signal Sources->
Noise

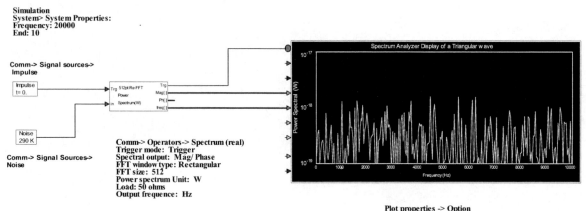

Comm-> Operators-> Spectrum (real)
Trigger mode: Trigger
Spectral output: Mag/ Phase
FFT window type: Rectangular
FFT size: 512
Power spectrum Unit: W
Load: 50 ohms
Output frequence: Hz

Plot properties -> Option
External trigger: 0
XY Plot X axis: 4
Grid line
Log Y

Exercise 2

Objective

To compare the spectrum of AM and FM signals

Lab Setup

Standard lab setup with VisSim installed

Introduction

When a carrier is modulated in any manner, sideband signals are generated. Sidebands are produced above and below the carrier frequency. For AM there are two side bands: $f_c + f_i$ and $f_c - f_i$, where f_c is the carrier frequency and f_i is the frequency of the modulating signal. In theory an FM wave has an infinite number of sideband frequencies spaced at multiples of the modulating frequency. This indicates an infinite bandwidth. The larger the multiple of these sidebands, the lower will be their amplitudes. After a certain frequency, the amplitudes or sidebands become negligible. In this exercise, the spectrums of these two types of modulation will be compared.

Procedure

1. Simulate the following system using VisSim. In this simulation, the frequency setting in the simulation properties should be at least two times the source frequency you want to see. Use the following blocks in this study:

    a) **Step**: Blocks > Signal producers > Step

    Settings:

    Time delay (sec): 0

    Amplitude: 1

    b) **Sine**: Comm > Signal sources > Sinusoid

    Settings:

    Frequency (Hz): 1

    Amplitude (V): 1

    Unit: Volt

    Phase output mode: Unwrapped

c) **AM Modulator**: Comm > Modulator Real > AM (real)

        Settings:

        Carrier Frequency (Hz): 10

        Amplitude (V): 1

        Phase output mode: Unwrapped

d) **FM Modulator**: Comm > Modulator Real > FM (real)

        Settings

        Carrier frequency (Hz) : 10

        Carrier Amplitude: (V): 1

        FM Deviation: (Hz/V): 1

        Phase output mode: Unwrapped

e) **Spectrum (Real)** > Comm > operators > Spectrum (real)

        Settings;

        Trigger mode: Trigger

        Spectral output: Mag / Phase

        FFT window type: Rectangular

        FFT size: 512

        Power spectrum Units: dBm/Hz

        Load: 50 ohms

        Output frequency: Hz

f) **Plot**: Use Toolbar button

        Options:

        External Trigger: 0

        XY Plot: X axis: 4

        Grid lines

        Log Y

g) **Simulation:**

    System > System Properties

        Frequency: 30

        End: 30

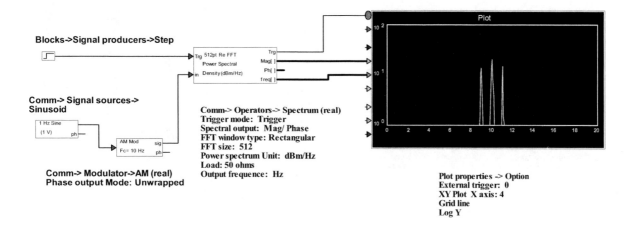

Simulation:
System->System properties:
Frequency: 30
End: 30

Blocks->Signal producers->Step

Comm-> Signal sources->
Sinusoid

1 Hz Sine
(1 V)   ph

AM Mod   sig
Fc= 10 Hz   ph

Comm-> Modulator->AM (real)
Phase output Mode: Unwrapped

Trg 512pt Re FFT
    Power Spectral
in Density (dBm/Hz)

Trg
Mag[ ]
Ph[ ]
f req[ ]

Comm-> Operators-> Spectrum (real)
Trigger mode: Trigger
Spectral output: Mag/ Phase
FFT window type: Rectangular
FFT size: 512
Power spectrum Unit: dBm/Hz
Load: 50 ohms
Output frequence: Hz

Plot

Plot properties -> Option
External trigger: 0
XY Plot X axis: 4
Grid line
Log Y

2. Measure the sideband frequencies, and check them against your calculation.

3. Replace the AM modulator with FM, and compare the frequencies of sidebands to those of the AM signal.

4. Use Carlson's Rule for calculation the bandwidth of FM as:

$$BW = 2(f_{deviation} + f_{modulation\ signal})$$

Compare calculation versus measurement from the following plot.

5. Write your conclusion and make a copy of your results for your instructor.

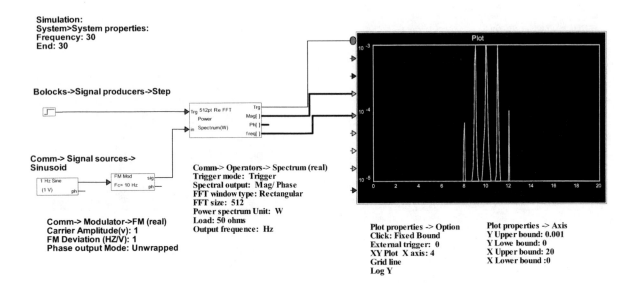

Simulation:
System>System properties:
Frequency: 30
End: 30

Bolocks->Signal producers->Step

Trg 512pt Re FFT
Power
in Spectrum(W)

Trg
Mag[ ]
Ph[ ]
freq[ ]

Comm-> Signal sources->
Sinusoid

1 Hz Sine
(1 V)   ph

FM Mod   sig
Fc= 10 Hz
ph

Comm-> Operators-> Spectrum (real)
Trigger mode: Trigger
Spectral output: Mag/ Phase
FFT window type: Rectangular
FFT size: 512
Power spectrum Unit: W
Load: 50 ohms
Output frequence: Hz

Comm-> Modulator->FM (real)
Carrier Amplitude(v): 1
FM Deviation (HZ/V): 1
Phase output Mode: Unwrapped

Plot properties -> Option
Click: Fixed Bound
External trigger: 0
XY Plot X axis: 4
Grid line
Log Y

Plot properties -> Axis
Y Upper bound: 0.001
Y Lowe bound: 0
X Upper bound: 20
X Lower bound :0

Exercise 3

Objective

To show the spectrum of the frequency sweep generator

Lab Setup

Standard lab setup with VisSim installed

Introduction

The frequency sweep block generates a frequency sweep according to the selected block parameters. The sweep start and stop frequencies, its duration, and the initial phase are specified. After the sweep is completed, a new sweep is started. This block outputs a real signal. The output spectrum of this block should show all the frequency components from start to stop.

Procedure

1. Simulate the following system using VisSim. In this simulation, the frequency setting in the simulation properties should be at least two times the source frequency you want to see. Use the following blocks in this study:

   a) **Impulse**: Comm > Signal sources > Impulse

   b) **Frequency sweep**: Comm > signal sources > Frequency sweep

   Settings:

   Start frequency: 1000 Hz

   Stop frequency: 10,000 Hz

   Sweep duration: 0.005

   c) **Spectrum (Real)** > Comm > operators > Spectrum (real)

   Settings;

   Trigger mode: Trigger

   Spectral output: Mag / Phase

   FFT window type: Rectangular

   FFT size: 512

   Power spectrum Units: W

   Load: 50 ohms

   Output frequency: KHz

h) **Plot**: Use Toolbar button

       Options:

       External Trigger: 0

       XY Plot: X axis: 4

       Grid lines

       Log Y

i) **Simulation:**

    System > System Properties

       Frequency: 100,000

       End: .01

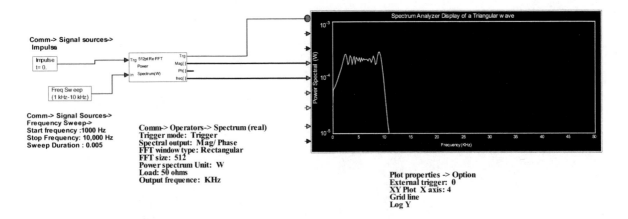

2. Measure the start and stop frequencies on the plot, and compare these with the setting of the block.

3. Change the start frequency to 10,000 Hz and the stop frequency to 30,000 Hz, and plot the spectrum. Write your conclusion and make a copy of your results for your instructor.

Simulation:
System-> System Properties:
Frequency: 100,000
End:.01

Comm-> Signal sources->
Impulse

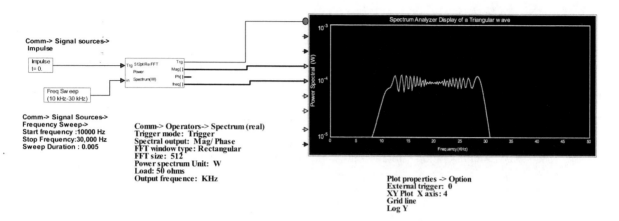

Comm-> Signal Sources->
Frequency Sweep->
Start frequency :10000 Hz
Stop Frequency:30,000 Hz
Sweep Duration : 0.005

Comm-> Operators-> Spectrum (real)
Trigger mode: Trigger
Spectral output: Mag/ Phase
FFT window type: Rectangular
FFT size: 512
Power spectrum Unit: W
Load: 50 ohms
Output frequence: KHz

Plot properties -> Option
External trigger: 0
XY Plot X axis: 4
Grid line
Log Y

Lab 5: Optical Fiber System Link Budget

Exercise 1

Objective

To calculate and simulate an optical fiber system link budget

Lab Setup

Standard lab setup with VisSim installed

Introduction

The link budget and usable bandwidth are the two critical factors in the design of a fiber optic link. The link budget is calculated to predict and adjust the power level of the light pulses arriving at the light detector.

The link budget takes into account a light power source, a light detector, and various cable and connector losses. Losses typical to fiber optic include: cable loss, connector loss, source-to-cable interface loss, cable-to-light detector interface loss, splicing loss, cable bend, aging device loss and link repair loss.

Mathematically, receive power is represented as:

$$P_r = R_t - \text{Losses}$$

P_r = Power received (dBm)

R_t = Power transmitted (dBm)

Losses = Sum of all losses (dB)

Procedure

1. Determine the optical power received in dBm and watts for a 20-km optical fiber link with the following parameters:

   — LED output power of 30 mW (Convert 30 mW to dBm)

— Three cable-to-cable connectors with a loss of 2 dB each
— Light source-to-fiber interface loss of 1.9 dB
— Four 5-km sections of optical cable each with a loss of 0.5 dB/km
— No losses due to cable bends
— No cable splices
— Fiber–to-light detector loss of 2.1 dB
— Assume no aging losses
— Assume no future repair

2. Simulate the following system using the following blocks.

   a) **Sine**: Comm > Signal sources > Sinusoid
      Settings:
      Frequency (Hz): 1
      Unit: dBm
      Power (dBm in 50 ohm) 14.8
      Phase output mode: Unwrapped

   b) **Av. Power**: Comm > Estimator > Av. Power (real)
      Setting:
      Load: 50 ohm
      Output: dBm for one of the block and W for the other one.
      Mode: running

   c) **Display**: Blocks > Signal consumer > Display

   d) **Gain (dB):** Comm > Operators > Gain (dB)

   d) **Plot:** Use toolbar button

   e) **System > System Properties**
      Frequency: 100
      End: 10

3. Compare your calculated received power both in watts and dBm with the simulated one. Print the output along with your calculations for your instructor.

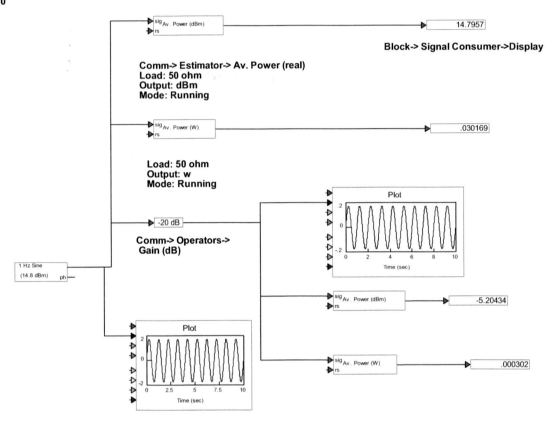

14.7957

Block-> Signal Consumer->Display

Comm-> Estimator-> Av. Power (real)
Load: 50 ohm
Output: dBM
Mode: Running

.030169

Load: 50 ohm
Output: w
Mode: Running

-20 dB

Comm-> Operators->
Gain (dB)

1 Hz Sine
(14.8 dBm)   ph

-5.20434

.000302

4. A fiber optic system is shown in the following figure. Calculate the output power required from the laser.

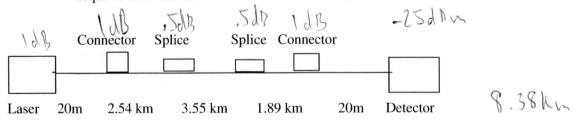

1 dB	1 dB	.5 dB	.5 dB	1 dB	-25 dBm
	Connector	Splice	Splice	Connector	
Laser	20m	2.54 km	3.55 km	1.89 km	20m	Detector

8.38 km

— The fiber used in the link has a loss of 2.5 dB per km. Its aging loss is negligible.

20.95 db loss

24.95 dB los

— The loss of the connector is 1 dB. Its aging loss is 0.1 dB.

— The minimum acceptable power of the detector is -25 dBm.

— The aging loss of the laser is 1 dB.

— Three repairs are estimated for the lifetime of the link, and each repair adds another splice.

— The loss for the splice is 0.5 dB. Its aging loss is negligible.

5. Simulate the above fiber system, and check your calculations with the simulated result. Print the simulation along with your calculation for your instructor.

Lab 6: Digital Modulation and Demodulation

Exercise 1

Objective

To generate ASK (Amplitude Shift Keying) and to measure its frequency spectrum

Lab Setup

Standard lab setup with VisSim installed

Introduction

ASK is the simplest method in digital modulation techniques. ASK is similar to AM except it has only two amplitude levels. The minimum required bandwidth is equal to bit rate.

Procedure

1. Simulate the following ASK transmitter system using VisSim. Two methods for generating ASK is used in this simulation. One method is to use AM modulator and the other is to use multiplication of PN code with a sine signal as carrier.

   Use the following blocks:

   a) **PN Sequence**: Comm > Signal producer > PN Sequence

   Settings:

   Shift register size: 6

   Output Mode: Binary (0, 1)

   Bit Rate: 2bps

   Internal clock

   b) **Sine**: Comm > Signal Sources < Sinusoid

   Settings:

   Frequency (Hz): 4

   Amplitude (V): 1

Unit: Volt

Phase output mode: Unwrapped

c) **AM Modulator**: Comm > Modulators (real) > AM (real)

Settings:

Carrier frequency (Hz): 4

Amplitude: 1

Initial phase: 0

Modulation Factor: 5

Phase output Mode: Unwrapped

d) **Multiplication**: Blocks > Arithmetic > Mul (*)

e) **Plot**: Use Toolbar Button

No settings

f) **Simulation:**

System > System Properties

Frequency: 100

End: 10

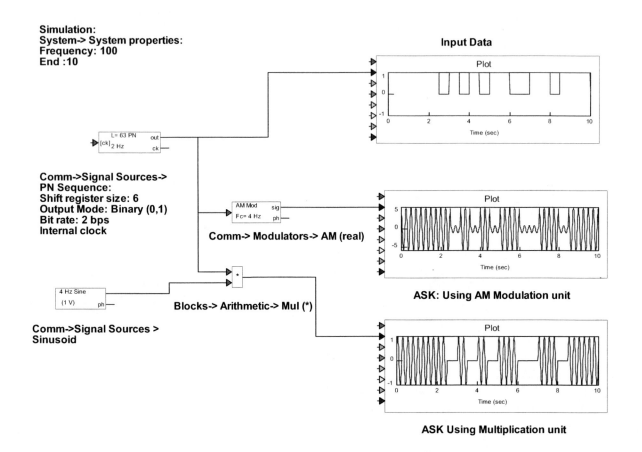

Simulation:
System-> System properties:
Frequency: 100
End :10

Input Data

Plot

Comm->Signal Sources->
PN Sequence:
Shift register size: 6
Output Mode: Binary (0,1)
Bit rate: 2 bps
Internal clock

Comm-> Modulators-> AM (real)

Plot

ASK: Using AM Modulation unit

Blocks-> Arithmetic-> Mul (*)

Comm->Signal Sources >
Sinusoid

Plot

ASK Using Multiplication unit

2. Compare the output of AM modulator with ASK modulation that uses multiplier unit. Explain how ASK is generated by the PN sequence, Multiplier and sine wave. Print the output along with your conclusions for your instructor.

3. Simulate the following ASK system, and measure the bandwidth using spectrum analyzer unit. In this simulation the following setting are needed for spectrum analyzer and the plot.

   a) **Spectrum (Real)** > Comm > operators > Spectrum (real)

   Settings;

   Trigger mode: Trigger

   Spectral output: Mag / Phase

   FFT window type: Rectangular

   FFT size: 512

Power spectrum Units: Watts

Load: 50 ohms

Output frequency: Hz

b) **Step**: Blocks < Signal producer < step

Settings:

Time delay: 0

Amplitude: 1

c) **Plot**

Fixed bounds

External trigger: 0

XY Plot: X axis: 4

Axis:

Y upper: 0.01

Y lower: 0.0

X upper: 10

X lower: 0

d) **Simulation:**

System > System Properties

Frequency: 100

End: 10

4. Compare the measured bandwidth with your calculation. Remember that fundamental frequency is half of the bit rate. Print the simulation and write down your conclusion for your instructor.

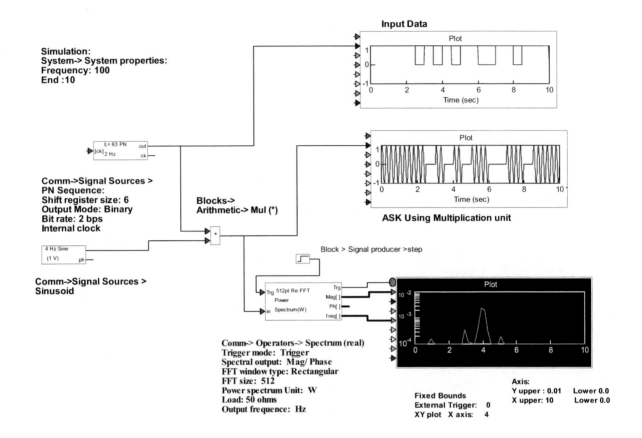

Simulation:
System-> System properties:
Frequency: 100
End :10

Input Data

Comm->Signal Sources >
PN Sequence:
Shift register size: 6
Output Mode: Binary
Bit rate: 2 bps
Internal clock

Blocks->
Arithmetic-> Mul (*)

ASK Using Multiplication unit

Comm->Signal Sources >
Sinusoid

Block > Signal producer >step

Comm-> Operators-> Spectrum (real)
Trigger mode: Trigger
Spectral output: Mag/ Phase
FFT window type: Rectangular
FFT size: 512
Power spectrum Unit: W
Load: 50 ohms
Output frequence: Hz

Fixed Bounds
External Trigger: 0
XY plot   X axis: 4

Axis:
Y upper : 0.01   Lower 0.0
X upper: 10   Lower 0.0

Exercise 2

Objective

To demonstrate the operation of the ASK (Amplitude Shift Keying) demodulation system

Lab Setup

Standard lab setup with VisSim installed

Introduction

ASK demodulation is the simplest method in digital demodulation techniques. The output of the transmitter is multiplied by the carrier and connected to the input of the integrator. The input signal is continuously integrated, and the integral output is periodically "dumped" and reset to a specified value. Therefore, those bit times that the carrier is present the, integrator adds the area under the curve. The square of the carrier will be maximum it will be zero in other places. The dump rate can be specified internally or through an external clock. The delay between the input bit rates and the output is due to the delay of the operation of the integrator.

Procedure

1. Simulate the following ASK transmitter and receiver system using VisSim.

    Use the following blocks

    a) **PN Sequence**: Comm > Signal producer > PN Sequence

    Settings:

    Shift register size: 6

    Initial state (Octal): 37

    Output Mode: Binary (0, 1)

    Bit Rate: 2bps

    Internal clock

    b) **Sine**: Comm > Signal Sources < Sinusoid

    Settings:

    Frequency (Hz): 4

    Amplitude (V): 1

Unit: Volt

Phase output mode: Unwrapped

c) **Multiplication**: Blocks > Arithmetic > Mul(*)

d) **Integrate & Dump**: Comm > Operators > Integrator (real)

Reset value: 0

Scale factor: 4

Dump Timing: External

Output mode: Held

Integration method: Euler

e) **Plot;** Use toolbar button

Fixed bounds

Axis:

Y upper: 1

Y lower: -1

X upper; 10

X lower: 0

f) **Simulation**

System > System Properties

Frequency: 100

End: 10

2. Write how demodulation operates and explain the delay in the output. Print the result for your instructor.

Simulation:
System >System properties:
Frequency: 100
End: 10

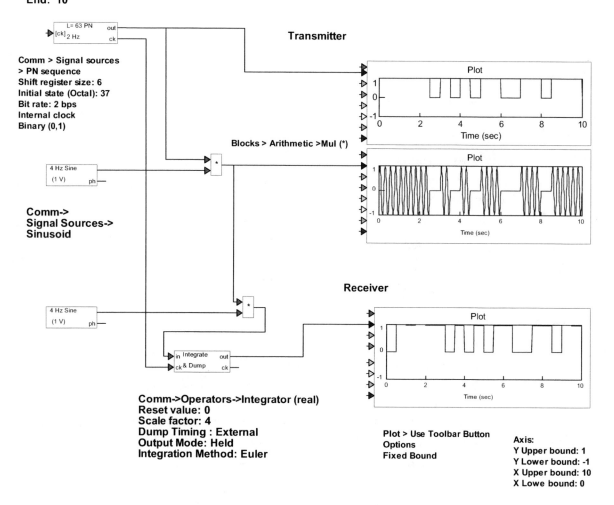

Comm > Signal sources
> PN sequence
Shift register size: 6
Initial state (Octal): 37
Bit rate: 2 bps
Internal clock
Binary (0,1)

Transmitter

Blocks > Arithmetic >Mul (*)

Comm->
Signal Sources->
Sinusoid

Receiver

Comm->Operators->Integrator (real)
Reset value: 0
Scale factor: 4
Dump Timing : External
Output Mode: Held
Integration Method: Euler

Plot > Use Toolbar Button
Options
Fixed Bound

Axis:
Y Upper bound: 1
Y Lower bound: -1
X Upper bound: 10
X Lowe bound: 0

Exercise 3

Objective

To generate FSK (Frequency Shift Keying) and to measure its frequency spectrum

Lab Setup

Standard lab setup with VisSim installed

Introduction

FSK is another simple method in digital modulation techniques. FSK is similar to FM except it has only two frequency levels. The minimum Nyquist bandwidth (BW) can be approximated by:

$$BW = 2(\Delta f + f_b)$$

BW = Minimum Nyquist bandwidth in Hz

Δf = Frequency deviation (difference between mark and space frequencies)/2

f_b = Bit rate in bps

Procedure

1. Simulate the following FSK transmitter system using VisSim. In the following simulation, two methods are used to generate FSK. In the upper part, two cosine waves with the frequencies of 4 Hz and 1 Hz as well as a not gate and two multipliers are used to generate the FSK. In the lower parts, the FSK modulator block with F1 = 1Hz and the frequency difference of 3 Hz are used. As you will see, the two results are the same. Use the following blocks:

   a) **PN Sequence**: Comm > Signal producer > PN Sequence

   Settings:

   Shift register size: 6

   Initial state (Octal): 37

   Output Mode: Binary (0,1)

   Bit Rate: 1bps

   Internal clock

   b) **Cosine**: Comm > Signal Sources < Sinusoid

Settings: Click Cosine

Frequency (Hz): 4 and 1

Amplitude (V): 1

Unit: Volt

Phase output mode: Unwrapped

c) **Multiplier**: Blocks > arithmetic > Mul(*)

d) **Step**: Blocks > Signal producer > Step

e) **Summing junction**: Blocks > arithmetic > Summing junction

f) **FSK Modulator (real):** Comm > Modulator (real) > FSK (Re)

Settings:

Number of tones: 2

Lowest Frequency: 1 Hz

Frequency spacing: 3

Amplitude(V): 1

Initial Phase (deg): 0

Phase output mode: Unwrapped

Phase mode: continuous

g) **Spectrum (real):** Comm > Operators > Spectrum (real)

Settings:

Trigger mode: Trigger

Spectral output: Mag/Phase

FFT window type: Rectangular

FFT size: 1K

Power spectrum unit: dBm

Load: 50 ohms

Output frequency: Hz

h) **Plot;** Use toolbar button

Fixed bounds

External trigger: 0

XY plot: x axis: 4

Log Y

Axis settings for spectrum plot

Y upper: 10

Y lower: 0.1

X upper; 10

X lower: 0

i) **Simulation:**

System > System Properties

Frequency: 1000

End: 10

2. Explain how the upper part of the simulation generates FSK.

3. Measure the bandwidth, and compare it with your calculation.

4. Print the result along with your conclusion for your instructor.

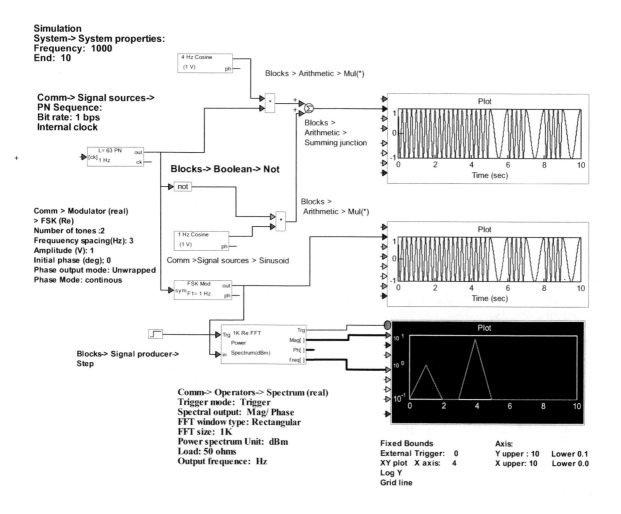

Simulation
System-> System properties:
Frequency: 1000
End: 10

4 Hz Cosine
(1 V)   ph

Blocks > Arithmetic > Mul(*)

Comm-> Signal sources->
PN Sequence:
Bit rate: 1 bps
Internal clock

L= 63 PN   out
[ck] 1 Hz   ck

Blocks >
Arithmetic >
Summing junction

Plot

Blocks-> Boolean-> Not

not

Comm > Modulator (real)
> FSK (Re)
Number of tones :2
Frequency spacing(Hz): 3
Amplitude (V): 1
Initial phase (deg); 0
Phase output mode: Unwrapped
Phase Mode: continous

1 Hz Cosine
(1 V)   ph

Blocks >
Arithmetic > Mul(*)

Comm >Signal sources > Sinusoid

FSK Mod   out
sym F1= 1 Hz   ph

Plot

Blocks-> Signal producer->
Step

Trg   1K Re FFT
      Power
in   Spectrum(dBm)

Trg
Mag[ ]
Ph[ ]
freq[ ]

Plot

Comm-> Operators-> Spectrum (real)
Trigger mode: Trigger
Spectral output: Mag/ Phase
FFT window type: Rectangular
FFT size: 1K
Power spectrum Unit: dBm
Load: 50 ohms
Output frequence: Hz

Fixed Bounds
External Trigger: 0
XY plot X axis: 4
Log Y
Grid line

Axis:
Y upper : 10   Lower 0.1
X upper: 10   Lower 0.0

Exercise 4

Objective

To study the demodulation of FSK (Frequency Shift Keying)

Lab Setup

Standard lab setup with VisSim installed

Introduction

There are different ways to demodulate the FSK signal. One way is to apply the modulated signal to the input of a high-pass filter. The output of the high-pass filter contains the information about the mark frequency. Then the signal is connected to the absolute value block and an integrator. This is similar to an envelope detector. The output of the integrator is compared to a threshold detector to differentiate between 0 and 1.

Procedure

1. Simulate the following FSK transmitter and receiver system using VisSim. Use the following blocks:

   a) **PN Sequence**: Comm > Signal producer > PN Sequence

   Settings:

   Shift register size: 6

   Initial state (Octal): 37

   Output Mode: Binary (0,1)

   Bit Rate: 1bps

   Internal clock

   b) **Variable**: Blocks > Annotation > Variable

   Name it : **Clock**.

   Connect it to the clock output of PN sequence

   In order to avoid long wiring connection, you can copy it to any place that you want to connect the clock.

c) **FSK Modulator (real):** Comm > Modulator (real) > FSK (Re)

Settings:

Number of tones: 2

Lowest Frequency: 1 Hz

Frequency spacing: 3

Amplitude(V): 1

Initial Phase (deg): 0

Phase output mode: Unwrapped

Phase mode: continuous

d) **Const**: Blocks > Signal producer > Const

e) **Time delay**: Blocks > Time delay > Timedelay

Initial condition: 0

Max buffer size: 4000

The amount of delay is set by the const block

f) **Butterworth High pass Filter**: Comm > Filters > IIR

Filter method: Butterworth

Filter type: High pass

Order: 4

Cutoff freq.: 4

Unit: Hertz

g) **Integrate & Dump**: Comm > Operators > Integrator (real)

Reset value: 0

Scale factor: 2

Dump Timing: External

Output mode: Held

Integration method: Euler

h) **Absolute block**: Blocks > Arithmetic > abs

i) **Threshold detector**: Blocks > Boolean

j) Plot; Use toolbar button

Fixed bounds

Axis:

Y upper: 2

Y lower: 0

X upper; 20

X lower: 0

k) Simulation:

System > System Properties

Frequency: 100

End: 20

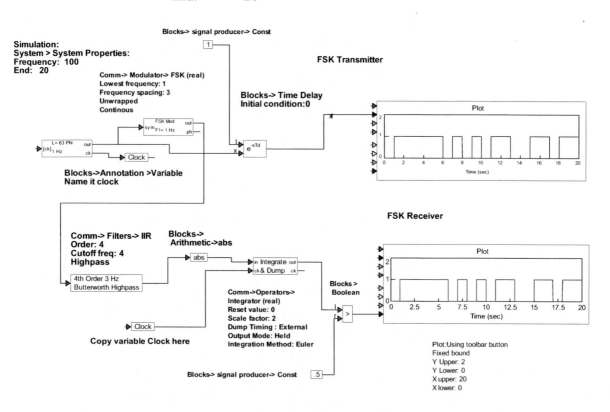

2. Explain why a delay unit is used to show the input sequence on the plot.
3. Print the plot, and write your conclusion for your instructor.

Exercise 5

Objective

To generate BPSK (Binary Phase Shift Keying) and to measure its frequency spectrum

Lab Setup

Standard lab setup with VisSim installed

Introduction

BPSK is another simple method in digital modulation techniques. BPSK is similar to PM (Phase Modulation) except it has only two-phase levels. The minimum Nyquist bandwidth (BW) can be approximated by:

$$BW = f_b$$

BW = Minimum Nyquist bandwidth in Hz

f_b = Bit rate in bps

Procedure

1. Simulate the following BPSK transmitter system using VisSim. In the following simulation, two methods are used to generate BPSK. In the upper part, one cosine wave with the frequency of 2 Hz along with multiplier are used to generate the BPSK. In the lower parts, the BPSK modulator block with $F_c = 2Hz$ is used. As you will see, the two results are the same. Use the following blocks:

   a) **PN Sequence**: Comm > Signal producer > PN Sequence

      Settings:

      Shift register size: 6

      Initial state (Octal): 37

      Output Mode: Binary (-1, 1)

      Bit Rate: 2 bps

      Internal clock

   b) **BPSK Modulator**: Comm > Modulator (real) > PSK > BPSK

      Carrier frequency: 2 Hz

      Phase output mode: Unwrapped

Amplitude: 1

Set the rest to: 0

c) **Cosine**: Comm > Signal Sources < Sinusoid

Settings: Click Cosine

Frequency (Hz): 2

Amplitude (V): 1

Unit: Volt

Phase output mode: Unwrapped

d) **Spectrum (real):** Comm > Operators > Spectrum (real)

Settings:

Trigger mode: Trigger

Spectral output: Mag/Phase

FFT window type: Rectangular

FFT size: 512

Power spectrum unit: dBm

Load: 50 ohms

Output frequency: Hz

e) **Step**: Blocks > signal producer > Step

f) **Const**: Block >Signal producer >const

g) **Multiplier**: Blocks > Arithmetic > (*)

h) **Summing junction**: Blocks > Arithmetic > Summing junction

i) **Plot:** Use toolbar button

Settings: Only for spectrum plot

Fixed bounds

External trigger: 0

XY plot: x axis: 4

Log Y

Axis:

Y upper: 100   X upper; 10

Y lower: 0   X lower: 0

j) Simulation:

System > System Properties

Frequency: 1000

End: 10

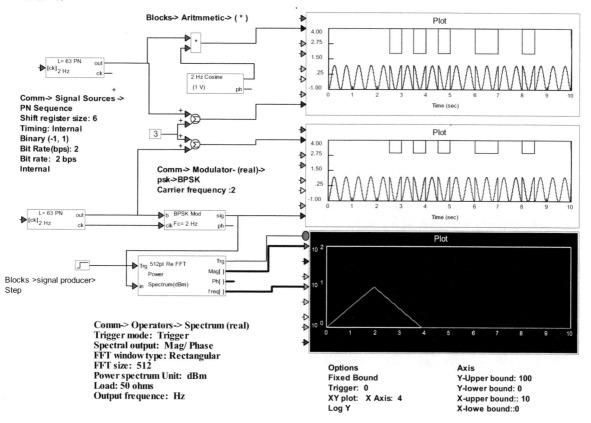

Simulation:
System > System Properties:
Frequency: 1000
End: 10

Blocks-> Aritmmetic-> (*)

L= 63 PN   out
[ck] 2 Hz   ck

Comm-> Signal Sources ->
PN Sequence
Shift register size: 6
Timing: Internal
Binary (-1, 1)
Bit Rate(bps): 2
Bit rate: 2 bps
Internal

2 Hz Cosine
(1 V)   ph

3

Comm-> Modulator- (real)->
psk->BPSK
Carrier frequency :2

L= 63 PN   out
[ck] 2 Hz   ck

b   BPSK Mod   sig
clk Fc= 2 Hz   ph

Blocks >signal producer>
Step

Trg   512pt Re FFT   Trg
       Power   Mag[ ]
in   Spectrum(dBm)   Ph[ ]
                      freq[ ]

Comm-> Operators-> Spectrum (real)
Trigger mode: Trigger
Spectral output: Mag/ Phase
FFT window type: Rectangular
FFT size: 512
Power spectrum Unit: dBm
Load: 50 ohms
Output frequence: Hz

Options	Axis
Fixed Bound	Y-Upper bound: 100
Trigger: 0	Y-lower bound: 0
XY plot: X Axis: 4	X-upper bound:: 10
Log Y	X-lowe bound::0

2. Explain how the upper part generates BPSK3. Measure the BW, and compare it with your calculation.

4. Print the result along with your conclusion for your instructor.

Exercise 6

Objective

To show how to demodulate BPSK (Binary Phase Shift Keying)

Lab Setup

Standard lab setup with VisSim installed

Introduction

The demodulator consists of the multiplication of the coherent carrier to the incoming modulated signal. This is the balanced demodulator. The result after the signal passes through the low-pass filter and the level detector is the demodulated sequence.

Procedure

1. Simulate the following BPSK transmitter and receiver system using VisSim. Use the following blocks:

   a) **PN Sequence**: Comm > Signal producer > PN Sequence

   Settings:

   Shift register size: 6

   Initial state (Octal): 37

   Output Mode: Binary (0, 1)

   Bit Rate: 1bps

   Internal clock

   b) **Const**: Block >Signal producer >const

   c) **Multiplier**: Blocks > Arithmetic > (*)

   d) **Less done** :Blocks > Boolean > Choose " < "

   The < block produces an output signal of 1 if and only if input signal x1 is less than input signal x2. Otherwise, the output is 0. On the connector tabs, "l" represents x1 and "r" represents x2.

   e) **BPSK Modulator**: Comm > Modulator (real) > PSK > BPSK

   Carrier frequency: 2 Hz

   Phase output mode: Unwrapped

Amplitude: 1

Set the rest to: 0

f) **Cosine**: Comm > Signal Sources < Sinusoid

Settings: Click Cosine

Frequency (Hz): 2

Amplitude (V): 1

Unit: Volt

Phase output mode: Unwrapped

g) **Butterworth Low pass Filter**: Comm > Filters > IIR

Filter method: Butterworth

Filter type: Low pass

Order: 4

Cutoff freq 1: 2

Unit: Hertz

g) **Plot;** Use toolbar button

h) **Simulation:**

System > System Properties

Frequency: 100

End: 10

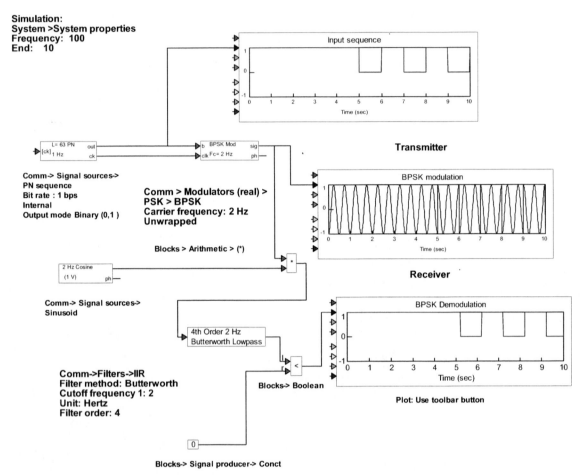

Simulation:
System >System properties
Frequency: 100
End: 10

Input sequence

Comm-> Signal sources->
PN sequence
Bit rate : 1 bps
Internal
Output mode Binary (0,1)

L= 63 PN out
[ck] 1 Hz ck

b BPSK Mod sig
clk Fc= 2 Hz ph

Transmitter

Comm > Modulators (real) >
PSK > BPSK
Carrier frequency: 2 Hz
Unwrapped

BPSK modulation

Blocks > Arithmetic > (*)

2 Hz Cosine
(1 V) ph

Comm-> Signal sources->
Sinusoid

Receiver

BPSK Demodulation

4th Order 2 Hz
Butterworth Lowpass

Comm->Filters->IIR
Filter method: Butterworth
Cutoff frequency 1: 2
Unit: Hertz
Filter order: 4

Blocks-> Boolean

Plot: Use toolbar button

0

Blocks-> Signal producer-> Conct

2. Print the result, explain the operation of the circuit, and write the conclusion for your instructor.

3. Use the BPSK demodulation block ,instead of the above method. Compare demodulated output with input data. Print a copy for your instructor.

Use the following blocks:

a) **Mag/Ph to Cplx**: Comm > Complex math > Mag/Ph to Cplx

b) **BPSk Detector**: Comm > Demodulators > PSk detector

Click on the QPSK icon and choose PSK Type: BPSK

This demodulator needs complex input. We use Mag/Ph to complex to convert the signal and its phase to complex for this unit.

Remember that clock synchronization is needed between transmitter and receiver.

Simulation:
System >System properties
Frequency: 100
End: 10

Transmit Data

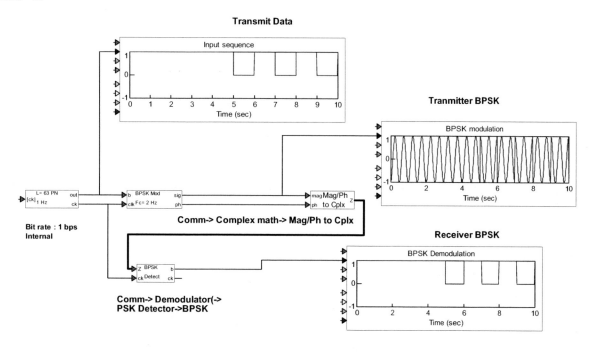

Tranmitter BPSK

Comm-> Complex math-> Mag/Ph to Cplx

Bit rate : 1 bps
Internal

Receiver BPSK

Comm-> Demodulator(->
PSK Detector->BPSK

Lab 7: Bit Error Rate and Noise Testing (Error Performance)

Introduction

The Bit Error Rate (BER) is the most common measure of error performance in a digital communication system. BER is defined as the probability that a bit is received in error. The Bit Error Rate (BER) is often used to measure the system performance as a function of Signal-to-Noise Ratio (SNR). Different amounts of noise are injected into the communication link, and the received signal is tested to judge the performance of the communication system at various SNRs. In this lab, BER is studied for different types of digital modulating systems.

BER Curve Control

Block Category: Comm > Estimator > BER Curve Control

This block is used to automatically vary the simulation's running time during multiple runs and to generate a BER curve. In order for this block to function properly, it is necessary to activate the **Auto Restart parameter in the Simulation Setup dialog box when more than one run is specified.**

The BER Control block allows up to 10 consecutive iterations of the simulation, each with its own simulation time duration expressed in seconds. The block accepts as input the current run Es/No value (from an AWGN block or other custom source) and the output error rate from a Bit Error Rate Estimator block. The input error rate estimate and Es/No value are recorded on the last iteration of each run. The block outputs a triggered (x, y) plot drive signal and provides a written BER summary notification message. **The (x, y) plot drive outputs should be connected to a plot block configured for external trigger, XY plotting and log Y scaling**. This block outputs the BER curve result at the end of the final run. **Care should be taken to match the number of runs in this block with those specified in the AWGN block (or equivalent) used.** The input and output of this unit is as follows:

E_b/N_0 = Run Es/No

Pe = Error Rate Estimate (Pe) [from BER block]

Trig = Trigger for BER plot [inactive until last run]

Y = Error Rate Results for BER plot [y-axis signal; use log scale]

X = SNR data for BER plot [x-axis signal]

Number of Runs: Specifies the number of simulation iterations. Valid range is from 1 to 10.

Mode:

Bit Error Rate: Forces the use of the Eb/No label in the results summary. Use this setting when providing a reference Eb/No input to the block.

Symbol Error Rate: Forces the use of the Es/No label in the results summary. Use this setting when providing a reference Es/No input to the block.

Duration: Specifies each run's duration in seconds. As the SNR is made larger, a longer duration is usually necessary to obtain a reliable error rate estimate.

Suppress Result Notification: When this option is selected, the automatic display of BER results at the end of the run is suppressed.

Show Results: Displays the last set results obtained using the BER Control block. The same message is also displayed at the end of the simulation.

Bit Error Rate and Symbol Error Rate

Block Category: Comm > Estimator > Bit, Symbol Error Rate

This block estimates Bit Error Rate (BER) by comparing a recovered data stream to a reference data stream. The block accepts both bits and symbols as input and can output either a BER or a Symbol Error Rate (SER). In order for this block to operate properly, the reference data stream must be delayed by the same amount as the recovered data stream. An external sampling clock must be provided to this block. Sampling at approximately the half symbol point is recommended. The input and output of this unit is as follows:

in = Recovered data stream

ref = Reference data stream

ck = External Clock (0, 1)

P_e = Error rate (Symbol or Bit)

num = Error count (Symbols or Bits) [Optional]

tot = Total count (Symbols or Bits) [Optional]

Count Start Delay: Specifies the initial delay in symbol counts before starting the error counting process. A symbol count occurs each time the sampling clock goes high.

Output Mode:

Symbol Error Rate: Indicates that the output error rate is the SER. When in this mode, regardless of how many bits within a symbol are in error, a single symbol error is recorded.

Bit Error Rate: Indicates that the output error rate is the BER. When in this mode, the actual number of bits that are in error within a symbol is counted. The total bits output displays the number of symbols processed times the number of bits/symbol.

Bits per Symbol: Specifies the number of bits per symbol. This parameter is only available when in BER mode

Important Steps for BER Simulation

a)   The "Auto Restart" option must be checked in the simulation setup for proper operation. Also, the stop time should match or exceed the longest duration value specified in the BER Control Block

b)   In the BER Control Block the user specifies the number of consecutive runs to execute and provides duration for each run (sec). The desired Es/No for each run is specified in the AWGN block along with the noise bandwidth (usually equal to the symbol rate). Note that the user must convert to E_s from E_b depending on the number of bits per symbol. In the future the number of bits/symbol will be a parameter. The BER Control block output signals for the output plot block.

c)   After the end of each run, the final bit error rate (from the BER block) and the run Es/No value (from the AWGN block) are read in and buffered to compile the BER curve results. Notice that the duration increases as the E_b/N_o value (SNR) increases. This is because fewer and fewer errors will be generated as the SNR is increased. Therefore, more time is needed to accurately estimate the bit error rate.

Exercise 1

Objective

To study the BPSK data communication system under channel noise

Lab Setup

Standard lab setup with VisSim installed

Introduction

In this exercise a BPSK digital communication system under different channel noise condition is studied. This system consists of a data source, BPSK modulator, AWGN (Additive White Gaussian Noise) channel, and a BPSK detector.

Procedure

1. Simulate the following BPSK digital communication system under channel noise. Use the following blocks:

   a) **PN Sequence**: Comm > Signal producer > PN Sequence

      Settings:

      Shift register size: 13

      Output Mode: Binary (0, 1)

      Bit Rate: 1 bps

      Internal clock

   b) **Integrate & Dump**: Comm > Operators > Integrator (real)

      Reset value: 0

      Scale factor: 1

      Dump rate: 1

      Dump Timing: Internal

      Output mode: Continuous

      Integration method: Euler

   c) **Variable**: Blocks > Annotation > Variable

      Name it: **ref**

      Connect it to the output of PN sequence after a delay.

In order to avoid long wiring connection, you can copy it to any place that you want to connect the data

d) **Const**: Blocks > Signal producer > Const

e) **BPSK Modulator**: Comm > Modulator (real) > PSK > BPSK

Carrier frequency: 10 Hz

Phase output mode: Unwrapped

Amplitude: .4

Set the rest to: 0

f) **Summing junction**: Blocks > Arithmetic > Summing junction

g) **Mag/ph to Cplx**: Comm > Complex math > Mag/Ph to Cplx

h) **BPSk Detector**: Comm > Demodulators > PSk detector

Click on the QPSK icon and choose PSK Type: BPSK

This demodulator needs complex input. We use Mag/Ph to complex to convert the signal and its phase to complex for this unit.

i) **AWGN Block**: Comm > Channels > AWGN (complex)

Settings:

Number of runs: 1

Symbol Rate: 1

Watts in 1 ohm

Run 1: E_b/N_0:   20 dB

j) **Delay (real):** Comm > Operators > Delay (real)

Delay Mode: Seconds

Delay time: 0.97

k) **Plot**: Use Toolbar Button

l) **Simulation:**

System > System Properties

Frequency: 100

End: 30

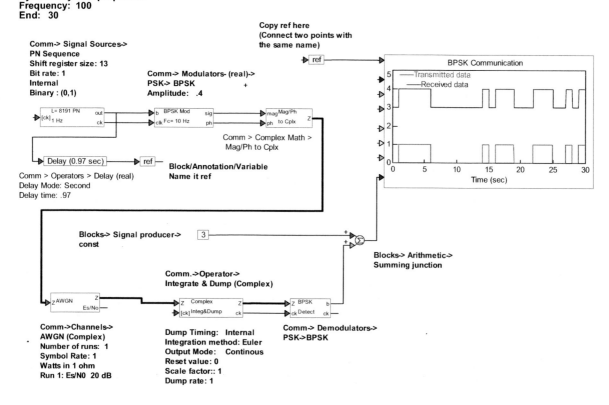

Simulation:
System->System properties:
Frequency: 100
End: 30

Copy ref here
(Connect two points with
the same name)

Comm-> Signal Sources->
PN Sequence
Shift register size: 13
Bit rate: 1
Internal
Binary : (0,1)

Comm-> Modulators- (real)->
PSK-> BPSK
Amplitude: .4

Comm > Complex Math >
Mag/Ph to Cplx

Delay (0.97 sec)

Comm > Operators > Delay (real)
Delay Mode: Second
Delay time: .97

Block/Annotation/Variable
Name it ref

Blocks-> Signal producer->
const

Blocks-> Arithmetic->
Summing junction

Comm.->Operator->
Integrate & Dump (Complex)

Comm->Channels->
AWGN (Complex)
Number of runs: 1
Symbol Rate: 1
Watts in 1 ohm
Run 1: Es/N0 20 dB

Dump Timing: Internal
Integration method: Euler
Output Mode: Continous
Reset value: 0
Scale factor:: 1
Dump rate: 1

Comm-> Demodulators->
PSK->BPSK

2. As you see in the output there is no error occur when E_b/N_0 is 20 dB. Change the ratio to 10 dB in AWGN channel and observe the errors.
    Check the following figure.

3. Why do you need a delay to show the transmitted data relative to received data?

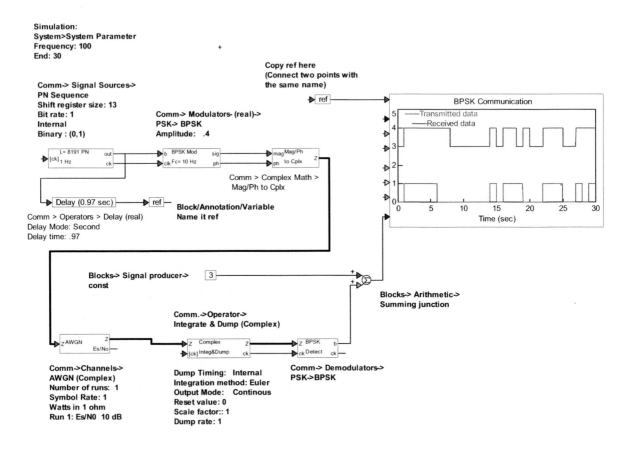

4. Why does decreasing Es/No in AWGN cause error in the received data?

5. Print a copy of your result, and write down your observation and conclusion for your instructor.

Exercise 2

Objective

To study BPSK communication system error performance

Lab Setup

Standard lab setup with VisSim installed

Procedure

1. Simulate the following BPSK digital communication system. The system consists of a data source, BPSK modulator, AWGN channel, and a BPSK detector. The rest of the blocks are for error performance measurement.

    Before simulation, activate the Auto Restart parameter in the Simulation Properties dialog window.

    Use the following Blocks.

    a) **PN Sequence**: Comm > Signal producer > PN Sequence

    > Settings:
    >
    > Shift register size: 13
    >
    > Output Mode: Binary (0, 1)
    >
    > Bit Rate: 1 bps
    >
    > Internal clock

    b) **Integrate & Dump**: Comm > Operators > Integrator (real)

    > Reset value: 0
    >
    > Scale factor: 1
    >
    > Dump rate Hz: 1
    >
    > Delay: 0
    >
    > Dump Timing: Internal
    >
    > Output mode: Hold
    >
    > Integration method: Euler

    c) **Variable**: Blocks > Annotation > Variable

    > Name it: **ref**
    >
    > Connect it to the output of PN sequence after the delay.

In order to avoid long wiring connection, you can copy it to any place that you want to connect the delayed data

d) **Const**: Blocks > Signal producer > Const

e) **BPSK Modulator**: Comm > Modulator (real) > PSK > BPSK

Carrier frequency: 1 Hz

Phase output mode: Wrapped (0, 2pi)

Amplitude: .3

Set the rest to: 0

f) **Summing junction**: Blocks > Arithmetic > Summing junction

g) **Mag/ph to Cplx**: Comm > Complex math > Mag/Ph to Cplx

h) **BPSk Detector**: Comm > Demodulators > PSk detector

Click on the QPSK icon and choose PSK Type: BPSK

This demodulator needs complex input. We use Mag/Ph to complex to convert the signal and its phase to complex for this unit.

i) **AWGN Block**: Comm > Channels > AWGN (complex)

 Settings:

Number of runs: 7

Symbol rate: 1

Run 1: 1 dB

Run 2: 3 dB

Run 3: 5 dB

Run 4: 7 dB

Run 5: 10 dB

Run 6: 15 dB

Run 7: 20 dB

Ref power Units: Watts: 1 ohm

j) **Delay (real):** Comm > Operators > Delay (real)

Delay Mode: Seconds

Delay time: 0.97

k) **BER Block : Comm > Estimator > Bit Symbol Error rate**

    Click: Output mode: Bit error rate

    Count start delay (Symbol): 100

    Bits per symbol: 1

l)   **Pulse Train**: Blocks > Signal Producer > Pulse train

    Delay: .97

    Time between pulses: .5

m) **BER curve control**: Comm > estimator > BER Curve Control

    Mode: Bit Error rate

    Number of run: 7

    Run 1 to Run 7 all: 100

n)   **Display**: Blocks > Signal Consumer > display

o)   **Plot**: Use Toolbar Button

    Plot properties:

    Fixed Bounds

    Geometric Marker

    External trigger: 0   (Bubble appear on the top input)

    XY plot: 4 (output X of Ber Curve control is connected to input #4)

    Log Y

    Grid line

    Axis:

    Y upper bound: 1

    Y Lower bound: 0

    X upper bound: 25

    X lower bound: 0:

p)   **Simulation:**

    System > System Properties

     Frequency: 50

     End: 10000

     Activate auto restart parameter

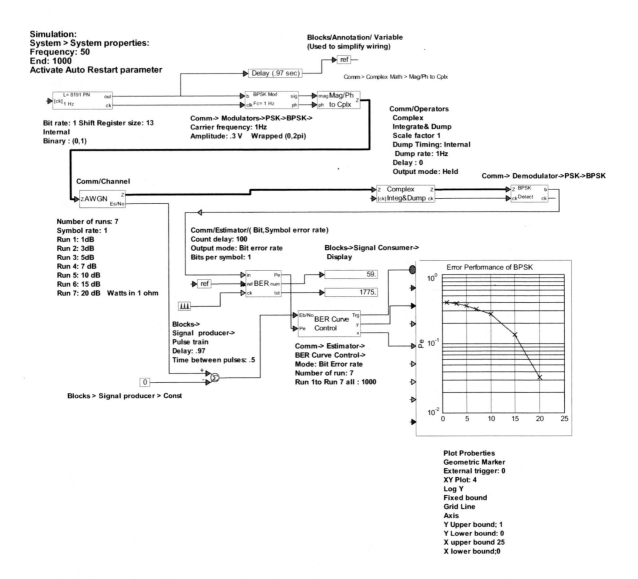

The Bit Error Rate result is shown in the following diagram. For each run, it shows the E_b/N_0 along with the probability of error.

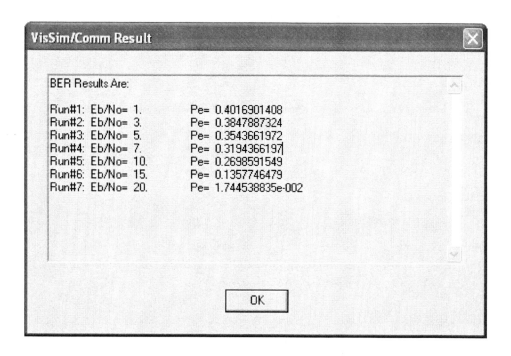

VisSim/Comm Result

BER Results Are:

Run#1: Eb/No= 1.   Pe= 0.4016901408
Run#2: Eb/No= 3.   Pe= 0.3847887324
Run#3: Eb/No= 5.   Pe= 0.3543661972
Run#4: Eb/No= 7.   Pe= 0.3194366197
Run#5: Eb/No= 10.   Pe= 0.2698591549
Run#6: Eb/No= 15.   Pe= 0.1357746479
Run#7: Eb/No= 20.   Pe= 1.744538835e-002

[OK]

2. Explain why the probability of error decreases as E_b/N_0 increases.

3. Print your result, and write down your observation and your conclusion for your instructor.

Exercise 3

Objective

To study a QPSK communication system under noise channel

Lab Setup

Standard lab setup with VisSim installed

Introduction

The system consists of a data source, QPSK modulator, AWGN channel, and a QPSK detector. Two data sources are used to represent two bits. These two bits are converted to symbols to make them compatible with the input of the QPSK modulator.

Procedure

1. Simulate the following QPSK digital communication systems. Use the following blocks:

   a) **PN Sequence**: Comm > Signal producer > PN Sequence

   Settings: For two PN sequence

   Shift register size: 13 and 14

   Initial state: 17,777 and 37,777

   Output Mode: Binary (0, 1)

   Bit Rate: 10 bps

   Internal clock

   b) **Integrate & Dump**: Comm > Operators > Integrator (real)

   Reset value: 0

   Scale factor: 10

   Dump rate Hz: 10

   Delay: 0

   Dump Timing: Internal

   Output mode: Hold

   Integration method: Euler

c) **Square wave**: Block > Signal Producer > Square wave

Frequency: 20

d) **QPSK Modulator**: Comm > Modulator (complex) > PSK > QPSK

Carrier frequency: 0 Hz. *It set to 0 when in complex envelop representation*

Phase output mode: Wrapped (0, 2pi)

Amplitude: 0.4

Set the rest to: 0

e) **Bits to Symbol**: Comm > Digital > Bits to Symbol

MSB: First

Number of input bits: 2

f) **Delay**: Comm > operators > Delay (real)

Delay Mode: Seconds

Delay time (sec) 0.101

g) **AWGN Block**: Comm > Channels > AWGN (complex)

Settings:

Number of runs: 1

Symbol Rate: 10

Watts in 1 ohm

Run 1: E_b/N_0:   21 dB

h) **QPSK Detector**: Comm > Demodulators > PSK (Choose QPSK)

i) **Plot**: Use Toolbar button

Fixed Bounds

Axis:

Y upper bound: 4

Y Lower bounds: 0

X Upper bound: 2

X lower bound: 0

j) **Simulation:**

System > System properties

Frequency: 1000

End: 2

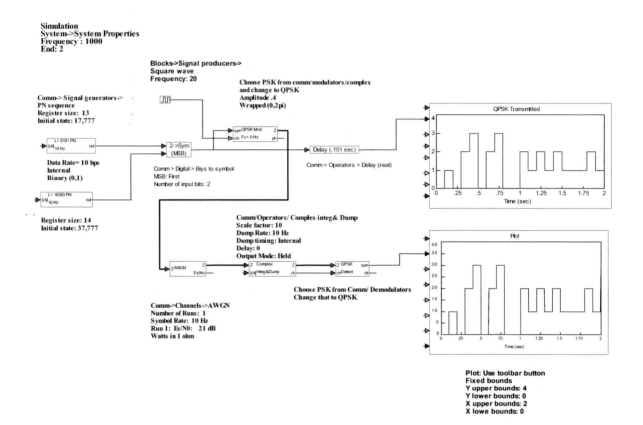

2. Reduce the E_b/N_0 in AWGN, and note any error in the receiver.

In the following figure the E_b/N_0 in AWGN is reduced to 3 dB

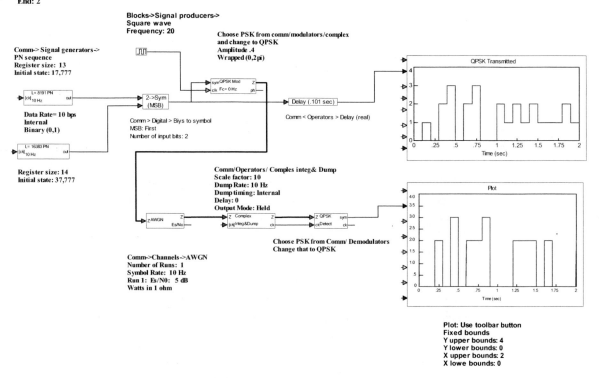

System->System Properties
Frequency : 1000
End: 2

Blocks->Signal producers->
Square wave
Frequency: 20

Choose PSK from comm/modulators/complex
and change to QPSK
Amplitude .4
Wrapped (0,2pi)

Comm-> Signal generators->
PN sequence
Register size: 13
Initial state: 17,777

L= 8191 PN
[ck] 10 Hz   out

Data Rate= 10 bps
Internal
Binary (0,1)

L= 16383 PN
[ck] 10 Hz   out

Register size: 14
Initial state: 37,777

2->Sym
(MSB)

Comm > Digital > Biys to symbol
MSB: First
Number of input bits: 2

sym QPSK Mod   Z
clk Fc= 0 Hz   ph

Delay (.101 sec)

Comm < Operators > Delay (real)

QPSK Transmitted

Comm/Operators/ Comples integ& Dump
Scale factor: 10
Dump Rate: 10 Hz
Dump timing: Internal
Delay: 0
Output Mode: Held

z AWGN   Z
Es/No

z Complex   Z
[ck] Integ&Dump ck

z QPSK   sym
ck Detect   ck

Choose PSK from Comm/ Demodulators
Change that to QPSK

Comm->Channels->AWGN
Number of Runs: 1
Symbol Rate: 10 Hz
Run 1: Es/N0: 5 dB
Watts in 1 ohm

Plot

Time (sec)

Plot: Use toolbar button
Fixed bounds
Y upper bounds: 4
Y lower bounds: 0
X upper bounds: 2
X lowe bounds: 0

3. Print your result, and write down your observation and your conclusion for your
    instructor.

Exercise 4

Objective

To study a QPSK communication system error performance

Lab Setup

Standard lab setup with VisSim installed

Procedure

1. Simulate the following QPSK digital communication system. The system consists of a data source, QPSK modulator, AWGN channel, and a QPSK detector. The rest of the blocks are for error performance measurement.

   Before simulation, activate the Auto Restart parameter in the Simulation Properties dialog window. All the settings are shown in the diagram.

   Use the same blocks as Lab 7 Exercise 2. The only difference is using QPSK modulation and demodulation instead of BPSK. Choose QPSK from Comm > modulator complex and change PSK type to QPSK.

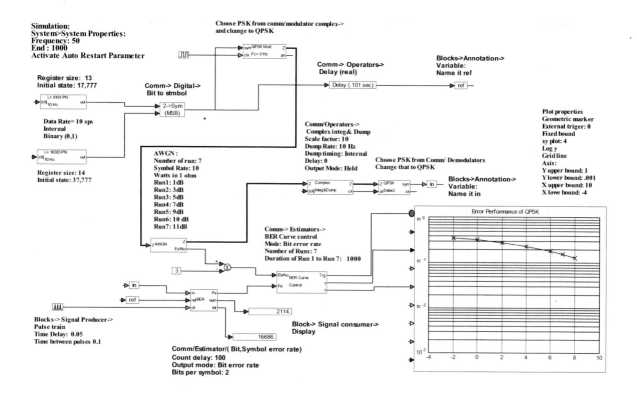

The Bit Error Rate result is shown in the following diagram. For each run, it shows the E_b/N_0 along with the probability of error.

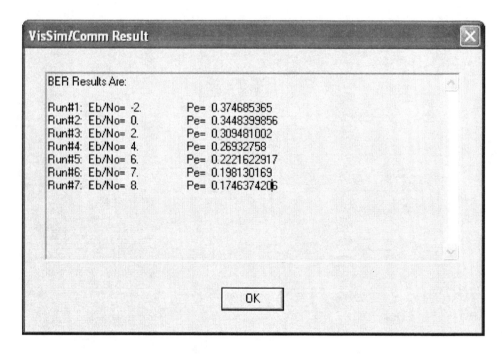

BER Results Are:

Run#1: Eb/No= -2.   Pe= 0.374685365
Run#2: Eb/No= 0.   Pe= 0.3448399856
Run#3: Eb/No= 2.   Pe= 0.309481002
Run#4: Eb/No= 4.   Pe= 0.26932758
Run#5: Eb/No= 6.   Pe= 0.2221622917
Run#6: Eb/No= 7.   Pe= 0.198130169
Run#7: Eb/No= 8.   Pe= 0.1746374206

OK

2. Explain why the probability of error decreases as E_b/N_0 increases.

3. Print your result, and write down your observation and your conclusion for your instructor.

Lab 8: Sample and Hold, Analog-to-Digital Conversion, and Compander

Exercise 1

Objective

To demonstrate the operations of a sample-and-hold (S/H) process under different sampling rate.

Lab Setup

Standard lab setup with VisSim installed

Introduction

The function of S/H circuit in a Pulse Code Modulation (PCM) system is to periodically sample the analog input signal and hold it. Then analog to digital converter convert those samples to a PCM code.

Sample/Hold (S/H)

Block Category: Blocks > Nonlinear > Sample Hold

The S/H block latches an input value under the control of a clock signal. At the occurrence of the pulse, the input signal (x) is sampled and held until the next pulse is applied.

Procedure

1. Simulate the following S/H system using VisSim. In this simulation three different sampling rates is used to show the output of S/H. Use the following blocks.

   a) **Pulse Train**: Blocks > Signal producer > Pulse train

   Generate three pulse train block.

Time delay: 0

Set time between pulses: 0.2, 0.1, 0.05 sec.

b) **Sine**: Comm > Signal Sources > Sinusoid

Frequency: HZ: 1

Amplitude: 1

Output mode: Sine

Units: Volt

Phase output mode: Unwrapped

c) **Sample/ Hold**: Blocks > Nonlinear > Sample hold

Initial condition: 0

d) **Plot**: Use toolbar Button

All default value

e) **Simulation:**

System > System properties:

Frequency Hz: 100

End: 3

Blocks-> Non linear->
Samplehold
Initial Condition: 0

Blocks-> Pulse Train
Time between pulses 0.2 sec

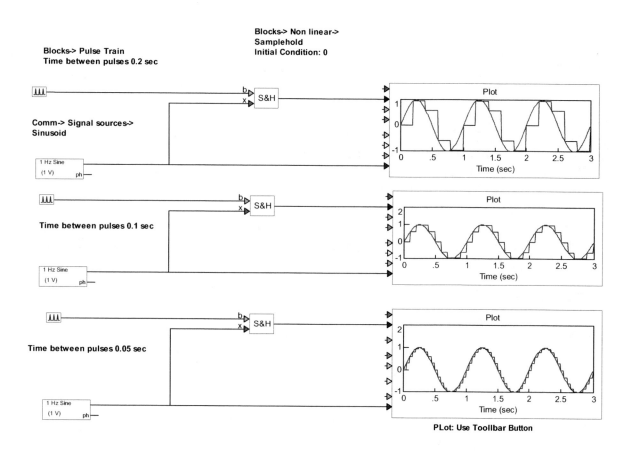

Comm-> Signal sources->
Sinusoid

Time between pulses 0.1 sec

Time between pulses 0.05 sec

PLot: Use Toollbar Button

2. Print your result, explain the operation of the system, and write down your conclusion for your instructor.

Exercise 2

Objective

To demonstrate the operation of Analog-to-Digital Conversion (ADC) process

Lab Setup

Standard lab setup with VisSim installed

Introduction

As an example of analog to digital conversion, the Symbol to Bits block receives a symbol as a voltage level in the input and outputs "n" parallel binary bit streams. The mapping is obtained by decomposing the binary representation of the symbol number. You can specify the number of output data streams. In this exercise, the output of the S/H circuit, which is considered a symbol, is connected to the input of the Symbol to Bits block to convert the different voltage levels in the input to three binary output digits.

Procedure

1. Simulate the following system using VisSim. Use the following blocks:

   a) Pulse Train: Blocks > Signal producer > Pulse train

   Time delay: 0

   Set time between pulses: 0.2sec.

   b) Sine: Comm > Signal Sources > Sinusoid

   Frequency Hz: 1

   Amplitude: 2

   Output mode: Sine

   Units: Volt

   Phase output mode: Unwrapped

   c) Sample/ Hold: Blocks > Nonlinear > Sample hold

   Initial condition: 0

   d) Summing junction: Blocks > Arithmetic> Summing junction

   e) Const; Block > Signal producer > Const

f) Variable: Blocks > Annotation > variable

    Name it Input. This is to avoid long wiring

g) Symbol to Bits: Comm > Digital > Symbol to Bits

    Bit order: MSB first

    Number of output bits: 3

h) Plot: Use toolbar Button

    All default value

i) Simulation:

    System > System properties:

    Frequency Hz: 100

    End: 3

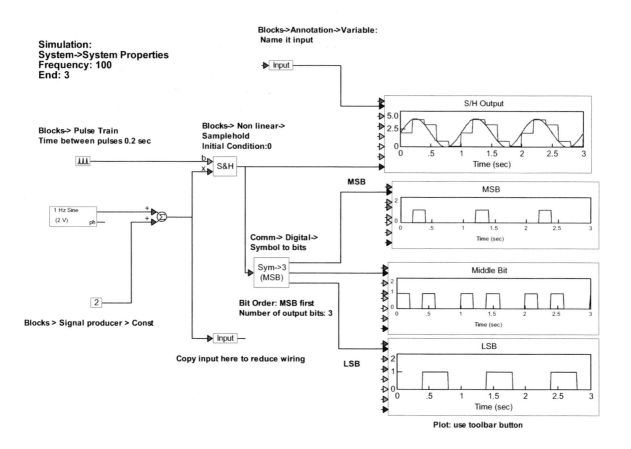

2. Check the output of the symbol to bits to see if the conversion to binary number was done correctly.

3. Print the result, and write down your conclusion for your instructor.

4. You can also use an ADC unit along with Symbol to bits to convert an analog signal to parallel digital output..

   ADC: Comm > Operators > ADC Set the following parameters in ADC.

   Number of Bits: 3

   Max. Amplitude: 4

   Center range Mode: Midlevel

   Output Mode: Unsigned

Simulate the following system using ADC.

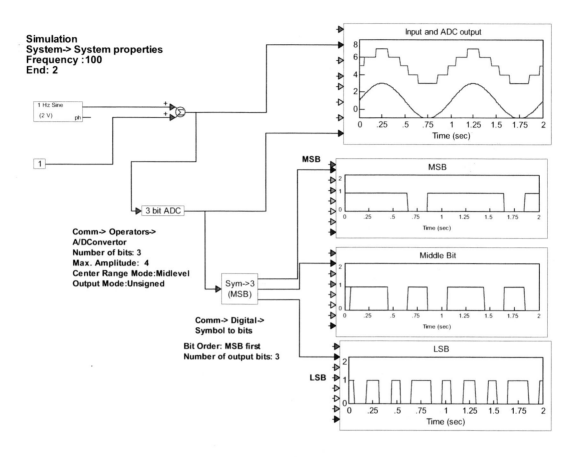

5. Check the output to see if the conversion to binary number was done correctly.

Exercise 3

Objective

To demonstrate the operations of compression using μ-law and A-law

Lab Setup

Standard lab setup with VisSim installed

Introduction

In nonlinear quantization, the input analog signal is compressed at the higher amplitude levels and expanded at the lower amplitude levels before quantization. Because the process involves both compression and expansion it is called companding. Companding is a means of improving the dynamic range of a communication system.

Compander Block

Block Category: Comm > Operators >Compander

This block implements signal companding and its inverse. Companding refers to a process of nonlinear amplitude compression usually performed prior to the A/D quantization of a signal. This process is employed when it is desirable to obtain a nonlinear quantization of the original signal. You can specify either μ-law or A-law companding. A standard value used in μ -law companding is μ =255; for A-law companding, A=87.56 is often used. Because the compander expects values in the range [-1, 1], the input signal is normalized by the Max Input Level parameter.

Compander Mode:

Compress: Indicates that the block is operating in compression mode

Expand: Indicates that the block is operating in expansion mode. This operation is the inverse of compression.

Compander Type:

μ –Law: Indicates μ-law companding

A-Law: Indicates A-law companding

Max Input Level: Indicates the maximum allowed magnitude (xmax) of the input signal. This value is used to normalize the input to the range [-1, 1]. When in Expand mode, Max Input Level scales the output.

μ- Value: Indicates the value of μ for μ-law companding. The value of μ must be > 0.

A- Value: Indicates the value of A for A-law companding. The value of A must be > = 1. A value of A=1 indicates no compression.

Procedure

1. Simulate the following system using VisSim. Use the following blocks:

   a) **Sine** > Comm > Signal sources > Sinusoid

      Use four sine waves to simulate a voice signal.

      Frequency Hz: 1, 1.6, 3.3, 0.4

      Amplitude: 1, 0.6, 0.4, .5 V

      Output mode: Sine

      Units: Volt   Phase output mode: Unwrapped

   b) **Summing junction:** Blocks > Arithmetic> Summing junction

      Add input to that. See Lab #2.

   c) **Variable:** Blocks > Annotation > variable

      Name it Input Analog Signal. This is to avoid long wiring

      Copy this unit any place that you need your input analog signal

   d) **Compander**: Comm > Operators > Compander

      Settings for three Compander:

      Compander mode: Compress

      Compander type: Mu-Law

      Max. Value 1

      Mu value: 255, 100, 2

   e) **Plot**: Use toolbar Button

      All default value

   f) **Simulation:**

      System > System properties:

      Frequency Hz: 100

      End: 10

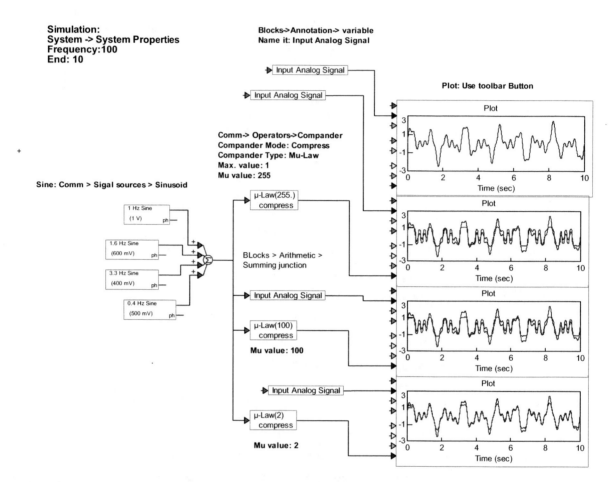

Simulation:
System -> System Properties
Frequency:100
End: 10

Blocks->Annotation-> variable
Name it: Input Analog Signal

Input Analog Signal

Input Analog Signal

Plot: Use toolbar Button

Comm-> Operators->Compander
Compander Mode: Compress
Compander Type: Mu-Law
Max. value: 1
Mu value: 255

Sine: Comm > Sigal sources > Sinusoid

1 Hz Sine
(1 V)   ph

1.6 Hz Sine
(600 mV)   ph

3.3 Hz Sine
(400 mV)   ph

0.4 Hz Sine
(500 mV)   ph

μ-Law(255.)
compress

BLocks > Arithmetic >
Summing junction

Input Analog Signal

μ-Law(100)
compress

Mu value: 100

Input Analog Signal

μ-Law(2)
compress

Mu value: 2

2. Explain the operation of the system, write your conclusion, and print a copy of the result for your instructor.

3. Change μ-law to A-law. Use the same compander and choose A law. Simulate the following figure. Do you notice any difference?

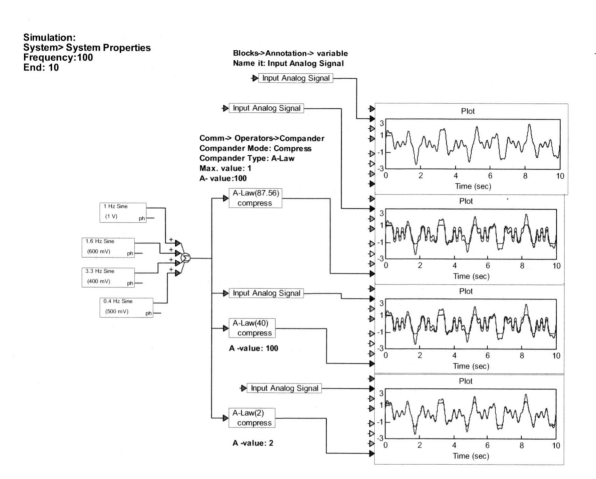

Simulation:
System> System Properties
Frequency:100
End: 10

Blocks->Annotation-> variable
Name it: Input Analog Signal

Input Analog Signal

Input Analog Signal

Comm-> Operators->Compander
Compander Mode: Compress
Compander Type: A-Law
Max. value: 1
A- value:100

1 Hz Sine
(1 V) ph

1.6 Hz Sine
(600 mV) ph

3.3 Hz Sine
(400 mV) ph

0.4 Hz Sine
(500 mV) ph

A-Law(87.56)
compress

Input Analog Signal

A-Law(40)
compress

A -value: 100

Input Analog Signal

A-Law(2)
compress

A -value: 2

Plot

Plot

Plot

Plot

Exercise 4

Objective

To demonstrate the operation of expansion using μ-law and A-law

Lab Setup

Standard lab setup with VisSim installed

Introduction

In the transmitter, the dynamic range of the analog signal is compressed, sampled and converted to PCM code. In the receiver, the PCM code is converted from serial to parallel, sent to digital-to-analog conversion, filtered, and finally expanded back to its dynamic range. In this exercise, the operation of expansion will be studied.

Procedure

1. Simulate the following system using VisSim. Use the following blocks:

   a) Sine > Comm > Signal sources > Sinusoid

   Use four sine waves to simulate a voice signal.

   Frequency Hz: 1, 1.6, 3.3, 0.4

   Amplitude: 1, 0.6, 0.4, .5 V

   Output mode: Sine

   Units: Volt

   Phase output mode: Unwrapped

   b) Summing junction: Blocks > Arithmetic> Summing junction

   Add input to that. See Lab #2.

   c) Compander: Comm > Operators > Compander

   Compander mode: Compress

   Compander type: Mu-Law

   Max. Value: 1

   Mu value: 255

   d) Compander: Comm > Operators > Expand

   Compander mode: Expand

   Compander type: Mu-Law

Max. Value: 1

Mu value: 1

e) Plot: Use toolbar Button

All default value

f) Simulation:

System > System properties:

Frequency Hz: 100

End: 10

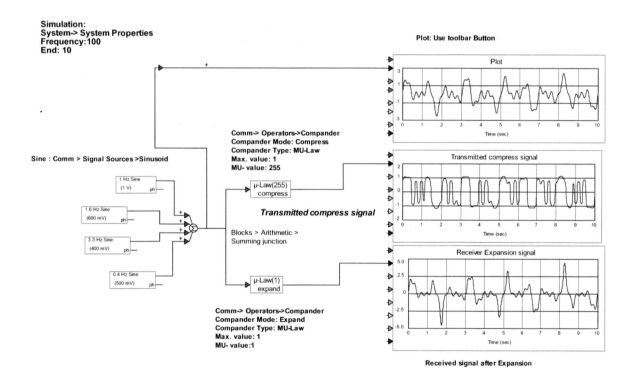

2. Explain the operation of the system, write your conclusion, and print the result for your instructor.

3. Change μ-law to A-law, see the following figure. Set the following for the Expand module:

> Compander mode: Expand
>
> Compander type: A-Law
>
> Max. Value: 1
>
> A - Value: 1

4. Do you see any difference?

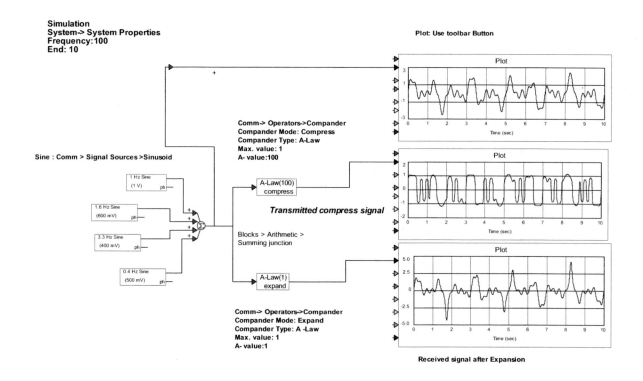

Lab 9: Pulse Transmission and Eye Diagram

Exercise 1

Objective

To demonstrate the effect of pulse transmission through a band-limited channel

Lab Setup

Standard lab setup with VisSim installed

Introduction

A perfect digital signal with absolutely square corners will look quite different when it passes through a band-limited channel. The corners will be rounded by the limited bandwidth of the channel. The signal will be distorted or tilted due to the unequal propagation delays of various spectral components. The amplitude will be reduced due to the attenuation effect of the channel. Noise is also added to the signal. All of these effects cause the receiver to recover the data with error. The narrower the bandwidth, the more rounded the pulse. If the phase distortion is excessive, the pulse will tilt and consequently affect the next pulse. This is called Inter Symbol Interference (ISI). The four major causes of ISI are:

- Insufficient Bandwidth
- Phase Distortion
- Amplitude Distortion
- Timing Inaccuracies

In this exercise, the effect of pulse transmission through a band limited channel will be studied. A band-pass filter and an attenuator are used to simulate a band limited channel. In this simulation the effect of band limited channel on a sine wave and square wave will be studied.

Procedure

1. Simulate the following system using VisSim. Use the following blocks:

   a) **Sine**: Comm > Signal Sources > Sinusoid

      Frequency(Hz)_: 1000

      Amplitude: 1

      Output mode: Sine

      Units: Volt

      Phase output mode: Unwrapped

   b) **Rectangular Pulses**: Comm > Signal sources > Rectangular pulses

      Pulse Frequency (Hz): 1000

      High level; 1

      Low Level: -1

      Duty Cycle (%): 50

      Start time: 0

      Pulse Mode; Duty Cycle

   c) **Summing junction**: Blocks > Arithmetic > Summing junction

   d) **Const**: Blocks > Signal producer > Const

   e) **Gain**: Comm > Operators > gain (dB)

      Set to -3 dB to represent attenuation in the channel

   f) **Butterworth Band pass filter**: Comm > Filters > IIR Infinite Impulse response.

      This unit represents limited channel bandwidth

      Settings:

      Type: Band pass

      Cutoff Frequency 1:   200

      Cutoff frequency 2:   3300

      Units: Hertz

      Ripple (dB): 3

g) **Plot**: Use toolbar Button

Fixed Bounds

Axis:

Y upper bound: 4

Y Lower bound: -2

X Upper bound: 0.001

X lower bound: 0

h) Simulation:

System > System properties:

Frequency Hz: 100,000

End: 0.001

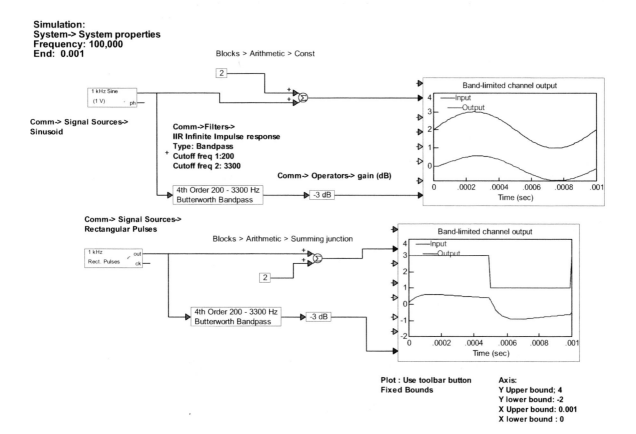

Simulation:
System-> System properties
Frequency: 100,000
End: 0.001

Blocks > Arithmetic > Const

2

1 kHz Sine
(1 V)   ph

Comm-> Signal Sources->
Sinusoid

Comm->Filters->
IIR Infinite Impulse response
Type: Bandpass
Cutoff freq 1:200
Cutoff freq 2: 3300

Comm-> Operators-> gain (dB)

4th Order 200 - 3300 Hz
Butterworth Bandpass   -3 dB

Band-limited channel output
— Input
— Output

Comm-> Signal Sources->
Rectangular Pulses

1 kHz   out
Rect. Pulses   ck

Blocks > Arithmetic > Summing junction

2

4th Order 200 - 3300 Hz
Butterworth Bandpass   -3 dB

Band-limited channel output
— Input
— Output

Plot : Use toolbar button   **Axis:**
Fixed Bounds   **Y Upper bound; 4**
                                      Y lower bound: -2
                                      X Upper bound: 0.001
                                      X lower bound : 0

2. Explain what happens when these two signal, the sinusoid and a rectangular pulse, passes through a band limited channel.

3. Add noise to the simulated channel by adding Additive White Gaussian Noise (AWGN) block. The settings for this is:

   AWGN > Comm > Channels > AWGN

   Number of runs: 1

   Watts in: 1 ohm

   Symbol rate: 1000

   E_s/N_b: 30 dB

4. Note the overall effect on the output

5. Print the output and write your observation and conclusion.

Simulation:
System-> System Properties:
Frequency: 100,000
End: 0.001

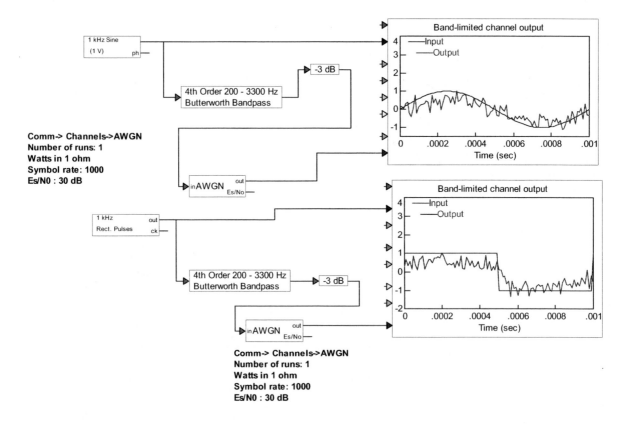

6. Increase the input frequency to 7,000 Hz, and observe the Inter Symbol
    Interference (ISI) effect on the output.

Simulation:
System >System Properties:
Frequency: 100,000
End: 0.001

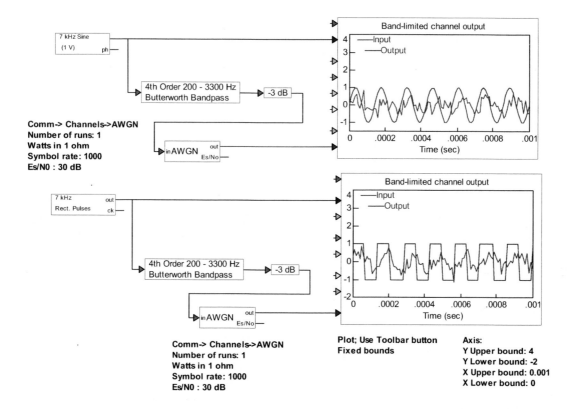

7. Explain the operation of the system, print the result, and write down your
    conclusion for your instructor.

Exercise 2

Objective

To demonstrate the eye plot generation and measuring performance of the pulse transmission system

Lab Setup

Standard lab setup with VisSim installed

Introduction

The eye diagram is the indicator that summarizes all the imperfections of the received signal bits in a pulse transmission system. Therefore, one way of determining the pulse transmission performance is through the eye diagram. This method is a visual evaluation of the state of the link. To form the eye diagram, all the signal bits are overlaid. In an ideal case, the eye diagram would be a perfect rectangle, and the overlap would cause the diagram to look like an eye.

The opening of the eye shows the separation of voltages for 1 and 0 bits. As the opening reduces, the voltage difference between 1 and 0 becomes smaller and therefore the probability of error will increase. The thick eye tops and bottoms mean the signal levels experience more noise.

The horizontal full opening of the eye diagram symbolizes the time required for the bits to be sampled in the absence of ISI.

Eye Plot

The eye plot simulates the use of an oscilloscope. Its applications include estimating S/N, detecting amplitude compression, and observing the effects of ISI. The following steps show how to configure a **plot** block as an eye diagram.

1. Click the right mouse button over the plot block to invoke its Plot Properties dialog box.
2. Click on the Axis tab, and do the following:
   - Activate the Retrace Enabled option.
   - In the Interval box, enter the desired interval.
   - In the Start and End boxes, enter the desired start and end times.
3. Click the OK button, or press ENTER.

Procedure

1. Simulate the following system using VisSim. In this simulation the channel is perfect that is no noise and no attenuation. As you see the eye is rectangle.

   Use the following blocks:

   a) **PN Sequence**: Comm . Signal sources > PN sequence

      Shift register size: 6

      Bit rate: 10

      Output mode: Bi-level (1, -1)

      Timing; Internal

   b) **Plot**; use toolbar button

      Options:

      Fixed Bounds

      Axis:

      Y upper bound: 2

      Y lower bound: -2

      X upper bound: 0.2

      X lower bound: 0

      Retrace Enable: 0

      Start time: 0

      End time: 10

      Interval: 0.2

      Timing Scaling: None

      Sub Plot count: 1

   c) **Simulation**

      System > System properties

      Frequency: 100

      End: 10

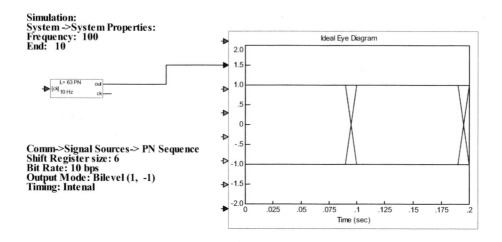

Simulation:
System ->System Properties:
Frequency: 100
End: 10

Ideal Eye Diagram

L= 63 PN   out
[clk] 10 Hz   ck

Comm->Signal Sources-> PN Sequence
Shift Register size: 6
Bit Rate: 10 bps
Output Mode: Bilevel (1, -1)
Timing: Intenal

Axis:
Y Upper bound: 2
Y lower bound: -2
X Upper bound:.2
X Lower bound: 0
Retrace Enabled
Start time : 0
End Time: 10
Interval: 0.2
Timing Scaling: None
End Time: 10
Interval: .2
Sub Plot Count: 1

Time (sec)

Plot Properties:
Options:
Fixed Bond

2. Explain why the difference between the eye top and bottom lines is 2 volts.

3. Why is the horizontal opening of the eye at 0.1 sec?

4. Connect the output of a PN sequence to the input of a Butterworth low-pass filter to simulate a band limited channel. Observe the effect on the eye diagram.

The setting for the filter is:

Butterworth Low pass: Comm > Filter > IIR

   Filter type: Low pass

   Filter method: Butterworth

   Order: 2

   Units : Hertz

   Cutoff frequency 1:   8

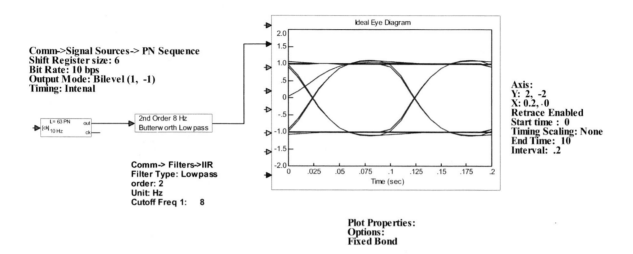

Comm->Signal Sources-> PN Sequence
Shift Register size: 6
Bit Rate: 10 bps
Output Mode: Bilevel (1, -1)
Timing: Internal

Comm-> Filters->IIR
Filter Type: Lowpass
order: 2
Unit: Hz
Cutoff Freq 1:   8

Axis:
Y: 2, -2
X: 0.2, 0
Retrace Enabled
Start time : 0
Timing Scaling: None
End Time: 10
Interval: .2

Plot Properties:
Options:
Fixed Bond

5. Change the cutoff frequency of the filter to 10 and 20 Hz, and observe the effect on the eye pattern.

6. Connect AWGN to the filter to add noise to the channel. Set the Es/No to 20 db. Observe the effect on the eye diagram. Explain why the vertical opening reduces.

    The setting of AWGN is:

    Comm > Channels > AWGN

    Number of runs: 1

    Symbol Rate: 10

    Ref power unit: dBm in 50 ohms

    E_s/N_0: 20 dB

7. Increase the Es/No to 30 dB. Explain the effect on the eye diagram.

8. Print the results, and write down all your conclusions for your instructor.

Simulation:
System-> System properties:
Frequency: 100
End: 10

Comm-> Channel->AWGN
Number of runs: 1
Symbol Rate: 10
REf. Power units: dBm in 50 ohms
Es/N0 dB: 20

Comm->Signal Sources-> PN Sequence
Shift Register size: 6
Bit Rate: 10 bps
Output Mode: Bilevel (1, -1)
Timing: Intenal

L= 63 PN
[ck] out
10 Hz ck

in AWGN out
Es/No

2nd Order 8 Hz
Butterworth Low pass

Comm-> Filters->IIR
Filter Type: Lowpass
order: 2
Unit: Hz
Cutoff Freq 1:   8

Ideal Eye Diagram

Axis:
Y: 2, -2
X: 0.2, 0
Retrace Enabled
Start time : 0
Timing Scaling: None
End Time: 10
Interval: .2

Plot Properties:
Options:
Fixed Bond
Grid Lines

Simulation:
System-> System properties:
Frequency: 100
End: 10

Comm-> Channel->AWGN
Number of runs: 1
Symbol Rate: 10
REf. Power units: dBm in 50 ohms
Es/N0 dB: 30

Comm->Signal Sources-> PN Sequence
Shift Register size: 6
Bit Rate: 10 bps
Output Mode: Bilevel (1, -1)
Timing: Intenal

L= 63 PN
[ck] out
10 Hz ck

in AWGN out
Es/No

2nd Order 8 Hz
Butterworth Low pass

Comm-> Filters->IIR
Filter Type: Lowpass
order: 2
Unit: Hz
Cutoff Freq 1:   8

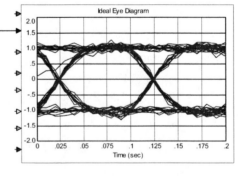

Ideal Eye Diagram

Axis:
Y: 2, -2
X: 0.2, 0
Retrace Enabled
Start time : 0
Timing Scaling: None
End Time: 10
Interval: .2

Plot Properties:
Options:
Fixed Bond
Grid Lines

Lab 10: Multiplexing and Demultiplexing

Exercise 1

Objective

To demonstrate the Time Division Multiplexing (TDM) and Demultiplexing

Lab Setup

Standard lab setup with VisSim installed

Introduction

Multiplexing allows the unused capacity of the channel to be put to use by other signals. In TDM, transmissions from multiple sources are interleaved in the same domain. In this exercise, several sources are connected to the multiplexer and then separated by the demultiplexer. Here, analog signals are used to demonstrate the action of the multiplexer and demultiplexer. In practice, a PCM system from different sources is time division multiplexed onto a single metallic or optical fiber cable.

Mux/Demul Block

Block Category: Comm > Digital >Mux/Demux

This block implements a digital multiplexer or demultiplexer. A multiplexer is used to combine several low-speed data streams into a single high-speed stream. A demultiplexer is used to reverse the operation. The block can be controlled by either an internal or external clock. At each clock pulse, the current active input (output) of the multiplexer (demux) is advanced by one in round-robin fashion. Typically, the block's clock rate (Switch Rate) should be equal to the number of inputs (outputs) times the individual line rate.

Number of Inputs/Outputs (n):

Specifies the number of inputs when in multiplexer mode and the number of outputs when in demultiplexer mode

---

Initial Position:

Specifies the initial state of the multiplexer or demultiplexer. The selected input (output) will be the active connection until the first clock pulse.

Mode:

Multiplexer: Specifies that the block operate as a multiplexer

Demultiplexer: Specifies that the block operate as a demultiplexer

Timing:

External: Specifies that the block be controlled by an external clock

Internal: Specifies internal timing control. See Switch Rate and Start Time below

Switch Rate:

Specifies the block's switch rate in hertz when in Internal Timing mode. This is the rate at which the block changes from one input (output) to the next.

Start Time:

Specifies the start time for the internal clock in seconds. This is the time of the first clock pulse.

Procedure

1. Simulate the following system using VisSim. Use the following blocks:

a) **Sine**: Comm > signal sources > sine

Generate four sinusoids:

Frequency (Hz):	1,	4,	7,	3
Amplitude (V):	1,	1.5,	1,	2

Unit: Volt

Phase Output Mode: Unwrapped

Output Mode: sine

b) **Const**: Blocks > Signal producer > Const

c) **Summing junction**: Blocks > Arithmetic > Summing junction

d) **Mux**: Comm > Digital > Mux/Demux

Generate two blocks.

Mode: Multiplexer	Mode: Demultiplexer
Number of lines: 4	Number of lines: 4
Switch rate: 1 Hz	Switch rate: 1 Hz
Timing: Internal	Timing: Internal

Start time: 0   Start time: 0

e) **Plot**: Use toolbar Button

    All default setting

f) **Simulation:**

    System > System properties

    Frequency: 100

    End: 10

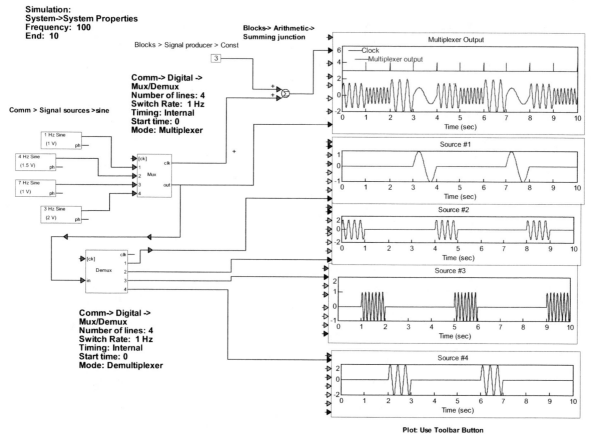

2. Explain the operation of the system, print the result, and write down your conclusion for your instructor.

Exercise 2

Objective

To demonstrate Frequency Division Multiplexing (FDM) and Demultiplexing

Lab Setup

Standard lab setup with VisSim installed

Introduction

In FDM, each signal is modulated onto a different carrier frequency. The carrier frequencies are sufficiently separated so that the bandwidths of the signal do not significantly overlap. In this exercise, four different signals are amplitude modulated with a different carrier. Each modulated signal requires a certain bandwidth centered on its carrier frequency, referred to as a channel. In the receiver side, these modulated signals are separated by different band pass filters.

Procedure

1. Simulate the following system using VisSim. Use the following blocks

   a) **Sine**: Comm > signal sources > sine

      Generate four sinusoids:

Frequency (Hz):	1,	4,	7,	3
Amplitude (V):	1,	1.5,	1,	2

      Unit: Volt

      Phase Output Mode: Unwrapped

      Output Mode: sine

   b) **Const**: Blocks > Signal producer > Const

   c) **Summing junction**: Blocks > Arithmetic > Summing junction

      Add more input. See lab #2

   d) **AM Modulator**: Comm > Modulators (real) > AM (re)

      Generate four AM modulators with different carrier frequencies

      Carrier Frequency (Hz): 4, 8, 12, 16

      Amplitude: 1

Initial Phase (deg): 0

Modulation Factor: 1

Phase output Mode: Unwrapped

e) **Butterworth Band Pass Filter**: Comm > Filters> IIR

Generate four filters with different cut off frequency 1 and 2:

Cutoff Frequency 1:   2,   6,   10,   14

Cutoff Frequency 2:   6,   10,   14,   19

Filter order: 8

Filter Type: band pass

f) **Plot**: Use toolbar Button

All default setting

g) **Simulation:**

System > System properties

Frequency: 100

End: 2

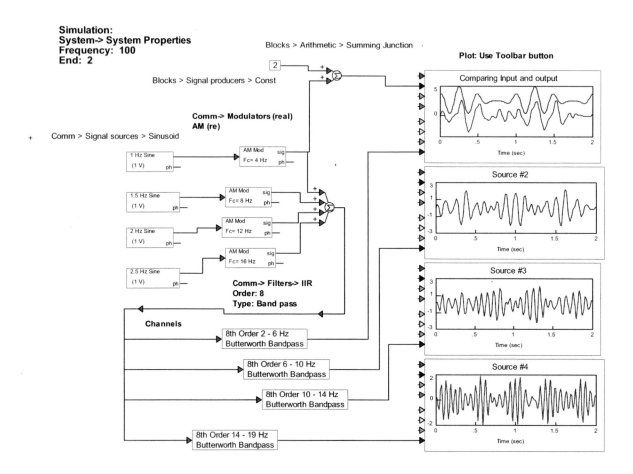

2. Explain the operation of the system, print the result, and write down your conclusion for your instructor.

Lab 11: Multipath Delay Distortion

Objective

- Simulate an FSK modulated multipath wireless communications channel.
- Vary the number of paths and discover and report the number of paths at which minimum multipath delay distortion occurs.
- Vary delay factor and record and report the delay at which maximum similarity occurs.

Lab Setup

PC with VisSim simulator

Theory

Multipath occurs when the transmitted signal follows more than one travelling path. These signals arrive at the receiver input at different time intervals because they have travelled different distances. The combined signal amplitude increases when the signals arrive in phase. When the signals arrive out of phase, the signal amplitude decreases and cause fading.

Multi Path Channel Block

Block Category: Comm > Channels > Multipath

This block implements a multipath channel, in which multiple time and phase shifted versions of a signal are modeled as arriving simultaneously at a receiver. Multipath channels are commonly used to model the interaction between a direct signal and multiple reflected path signals. The reflected signals affect both the amplitude and phase of the received signal. Block parameters include the number of total paths, and the individual path's delay, relative gain, and phase rotation. This block takes a complex signal as:
x = Complex input signal [Re, Im]
y = Complex output signal [Re, Im]

Number of Paths

    Specifies the number of paths in the model. Up to four paths may be specified.

Initial Condition (Real)

    Specifies the Real component initial condition for the internal shift register used by the model.

Initial Condition (Imag)

    Specifies the Imaginary component initial condition for the internal shift register used by the model.

Delay Mode

    Sim Steps

        Indicates the path delays are specified in simulation steps.

    Seconds

        Indicates the path delays are specified in seconds.

Path Delay

    Specifies the delay in seconds or simulation steps associated with each path in the channel model.

Weight

    Specifies a relative weight for each of the model paths. This value is not in dB.

Phase Rotation

    Specifies the phase rotation in degrees associated with each path.

Complex tone

Block Category: Comm > Signal Sources > Complex tone

This block generates a rotating complex phasor according to selected block parameters.

The internal generator phase (in radians) is also available as an output.

y1 = Complex output signal [Re, Im]

y2 = Generator phase (rad) [Optional]

Frequency

    Indicates the frequency fc, in hertz, of the complex tone.

Amplitude / Power

    Indicates the amplitude A, in volts, of the complex tone, or depending on the Units setting, the complex power of the tone in milli-decibels (50 Ohms).

Initial Phase

    Indicates the starting phase of the complex tone. This value is specified in degrees.

Units

> **Volts**
>
>> Indicates that the signal amplitude is specified in volts.
>
> **dBm**
>
>> Indicates that the signal complex power is specified in milli-decibels (50 Ohm load).

Max Index

Block category: Comm > Operators > Max Index

This block returns the index of the largest input signal. The block can be configured to accept up to 16 inputs. A typical application of this block is in the creation of M-ary decision circuits (e.g. detection of MFSK). Should two or more inputs share the largest value; the output index will be that of the lowest input connection in the set.

Number of Inputs

> Specifies the number of input connections N. Valid range is 2 to 16.

Index Mode

> *Start at Zero*
>
> Specifies the output range to be {0, 1,... N-1}.
>
> *Start at One*
>
> Specifies the output range to be {1, 2, .. N}.

Procedures

1. Simulate the following system using VisSim. Using the following blocks:

    a) Insert a random symbol generator (Comm> Signal Sources > Random Symbol) as input data and set it as follows

Timing: Internal	Number of symbols: 4
Symbol Rate (sps): 500	Start time: 0

    The number of symbols is four for 4-ary FSK input.

    b) Add an FSK modulator (Comm> Modulator) and set it as follows:

    Number of tones: 4

    Lowest frequency (Hz): 1000

    Frequency spacing (Hz): 500

    Amplitude (V): 1

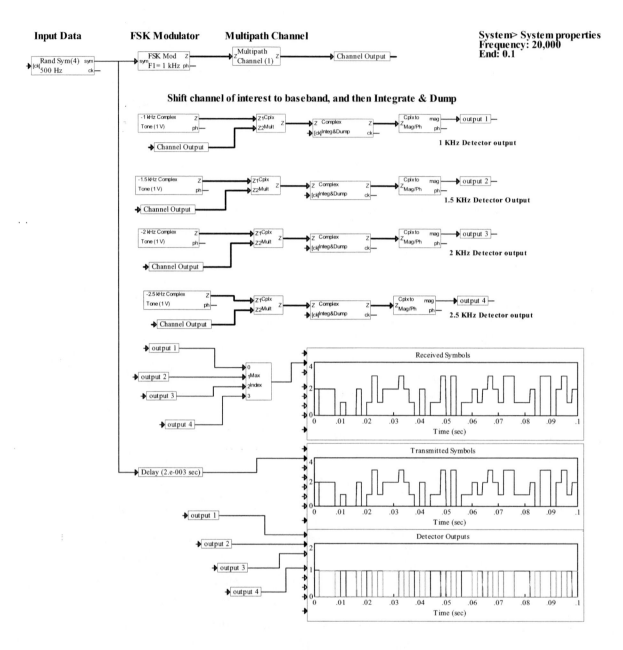

Phase output Mode: Unwrapped   Phase Mode: Continuous

The FSK modulator is configured for 4-ary output, with 1 KHz as the lowest tone and 500 Hz spacing between tones. The four tones are 1, 1.5, 2 and 2.5 KHz

c) Insert a multipath channel (Comm> Channel > Multipath) and connect it as indicated in the circuit diagram. For the first run assume that there is no multipath and set the parameters as follows:

Number of paths: 1

Initial condition (Img): 0

	Path delay (sec)	Weight	Phase rotation
Path #1	0	1	0

You can choose up to four paths. Later you can change the amount of weight and phase rotation for each path to study their effect...

d) In order to avoid crowded wiring, use variable block (Blocks>Annotation>Variable) and name them properly. As an example in this figure a variable with the name of "Channel Output" is used and you can use this variable with the same name in other places in the diagram without connecting them via the wire.

e) In order to recover the symbols, four detectors are used. In each of these detectors the following units are needed.

1) Multiplication of the FSK signal with proper carrier. The output of the FSK modulator is complex, four complex tone generators are needed as shown in the following figure. The complex tone (Comm/Signal Sources > Complex tone) connected to the Z1 input of complex multiplier (Comm >Complex Math > Multiplication). The settings of four complex tones are:

Frequency (Hz): -1000,   -1500,   -2000,   -2500

Notice the negative sign for frequencies.

Amplitude: 1   Initial phase (deg): 0

Phase output: mode: Unwrapped   Units: Volts

The other input of the multiplier Z2 is connected to Z output of the Multipath channel by **Channel output** variable.

2) The output of the multiplier is connected to the complex integrate and dump (Comm>Operators > Integrator & Dump complex) unit. The complex integrator and damp continuously integrate the input signal and

periodically dumped and reset to a specified value for symbol recovery. Set the parameters of this unit as follows:

Dump Timing: Internal	Reset value: 0
Scale factor: 500	Output Mode: Held
Dump rate: 500	Integration method: Euler
Initial Delay (sec): 0	

3) In order to show the output on the plot a complex to magnitude and phase (Comm> Complex Math > Complex to Mag / phase) unit is used. The magnitude output of this unit is connected to one of the inputs of the plot by four variable with the name of output1 to output4. This is to save wiring.

f) The largest output value among these four integrators is the demodulated symbol. Therefore in order to detect the FSK signal, the outputs of the complex to magnitude blocks are connected to the inputs of the maximum index block (Comm>Operators>Max index). This block returns the index of the largest input signal. The block can be configured to accept up to 16 inputs. A typical application of this block is in the creation of M-ary decision circuits (e.g. detection of MFSK). Should two or more inputs share the largest value; the output index will be that of the lowest input connection in the set. Set the parameters of this block as follows:

Number of inputs: 4   Index Mode: Starts at zero

g) Insert a real delay function (Comm > Operators > Delay (real)) as indicated in the diagram. Set the delay to 2e-0.003 seconds and set the Delay Mode to second. The delay is used because of the delay in integrator and dump unit. This delay makes input and the output plot on the same time reference.

h) Plot: use Toolbar Button and set it as follows:

    Options:

        Fixed bounds

    Axis:

        Y Upper bound: 4 and 2 for the last plot
        Y Lower bound: 0
        X upper bound: 0.1
        X lower bound: 0

i) Run the simulation under the following properties:

Choose System > System Properties

Frequency: 20,000

End: 0.1

J) In the first run you do not observe multipath effects since only one path exist,

k) Vary the number of multipath channels and run with different path delay, weight and phase rotation. Observe changes in the output

l) Vary the amount of delay in the delay function and attempt to achieve maximum similarity.

m) As extra exercise, in VisSim, these detectors can be constructed as compound blocks. The compound blocks are used to avoid crowded figure and wiring. This is shown in next figure

The following procedure shows how to create a compound block:

1. Select the blocks to be encapsulated.

2. Choose Edit > Create Compound Block

3. Avoid using the dot (.) character in the name. VisSim uses it to separate compound block

4. Under compound name, enter a name (e.g. 1 KHz Detector). names in the title bar. The default name is compound.

5. Click on the OK button, or press Enter.

Conclusion /Observation

1. Describe the effect on the demodulated signal by varying the number of multipath channels

2. Describe the effect of varying the delay in multipath unit. Did you achieve maximum similarity? If so, at what value of delay?

3. Print the result and write down your conclusion for your instructor.

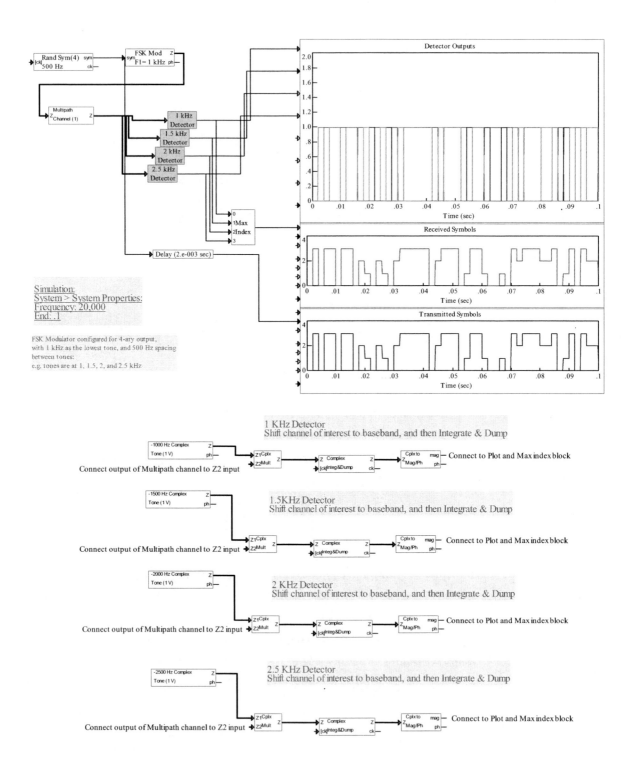

Lab 12: BPSK Signal Generation, Multiple Access and Recovery

Exercise 1

Objective

Generate the BPSK signals that are to be multiplexed using an FDMA system.

Lab Setup

Standard lab setup with VisSim installed

Introduction

In this lab BPSK signals are used to generate Frequency Division Multiple Access (FDMA) system. BPSK signals can be generated by multiplying the NRZ bipolar digital sequence directly with the carrier. In this lab three different BPSK signals are generated from baseband NRZ codes.

Procedure

1. Simulate the following system using VisSim. Use the following blocks:

   a) **Sine**: Comm > signal sources > sine

   Generate three sinusoids as the carrier.

   Frequency (Hz):   1

   Amplitude (V):   1

   Unit: Volt

   Phase Output Mode: Unwrapped

   Output Mode: sine

   Timing: Internal

   Timing: Internal

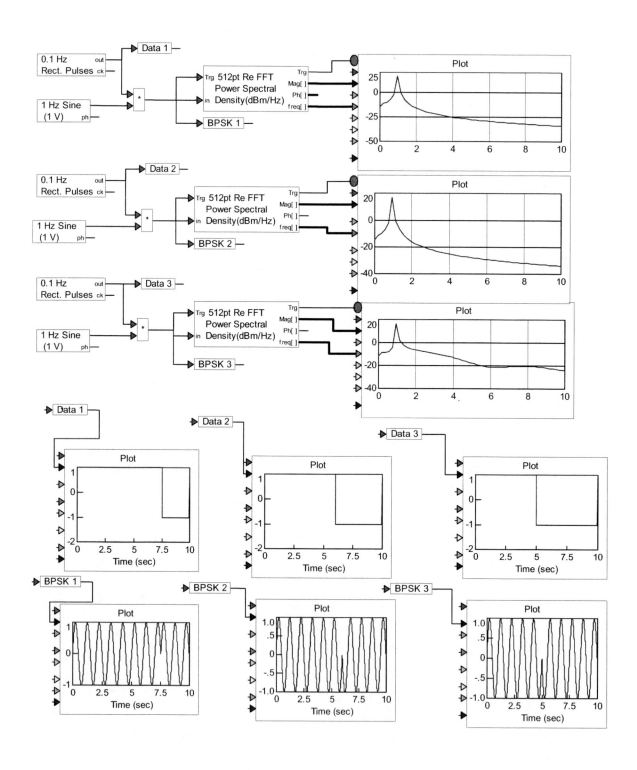

b) Use three 0.1Hz rectangular pulses (Comm> Signal sources > Rectangular Pulse) with different duty cycles, as the NRZ digital data sources. Make sure that the high voltage is +1 and the low voltage is -1. Set the pulse mode to duty cycle. For example the percent of duty cycles could be 75, 60 and 50.

c) Connect the carrier (Sinusoid) and the data signal to the multiplier (Blocks> Arithmetic > *) to generate the BPSK signal

d) Use the spectrum block (real) (Comm > Operators> Spectrum real) to obtain the spectrum of the BPSK signal. Set the following for this unit:

Trigger mode: Continuous	Spectral Output: Mag/Phase FFT
Window type: Rectangular	FFT size: 512
Power Spectrum Unit: dBm/Hz	Load: 50 ohms
Output Frequency unit: Hz	Number of FFT Av: 1

e) Connect the Spectrum analyzer block to display. Use the following setting for the display unit.

Fixer Bound

External trigger: 0	The input with Bubble is input #0
XY Plot X-axis: 4	Output frequency of spectrum block connected to input #4

Axis

Y-Upper Bound: 20	X-Upper Bound: 10
Y Lower bound: -50	X Lower bound: 0

f) Use six plot blocks to plot the different digital data, and BPSK-modulated waveforms for the three modulators.

g) In order to avoid crowded wires use variable (Blocks> Annotation>variable) and name them properly as Data 1, Data 2, Data 3, BPSK 1,BPSK 2 and BPSK 3
Connect them to proper outputs and inputs.

h) Simulate the circuit, and run the design. Use the following simulation properties.
System > System Properties

Frequency: 100 Hz

End: 10

1. Conclusion/Observation

1. Plot and store the graphs. Measure the main frequency components of BPSK signal using the spectrum plot. In order to measure the peaks of the plot use the following procedure:

   1) Double click on the plot

   2) Click on the read the coordinate

   3) Use mouse and move on the peak and read the coordinates X and Y

   Compare your measurement with your expectation.

2. Three BPSK waveform are generated that can be given as input to the FDMA system

3. Write down your observation and explain the operation of the system and prepare a copy for your instructor.

Exercise 2

Objective

Simulate and analyze the FDMA system using BPSK modulation

Lab Setup

Standard lab setup with VisSim installed

Introduction

In an FDMA system, the different voice and data signals that occupy the same bandwidth in the frequency spectrum are converted to different frequency bands that do not interfere with each other. These signals are then mixed and sent along the channel. In effect, the available frequency is divided into different channels to which different baseband voice signals are accommodated.

Since different signals occupy different frequency bands, there is no interference and continuous data flow can exist between the transmitter and the receiver.

In this simulation the three BPSK signals that are generated in previous exercise are modulated with three different frequencies to construct an FDMA system.

Procedure

1. Simulate the following system using VisSim. Use the following blocks:

   a) The BPSK signal generation is the same as lab 12 Exercise 1 and repeated here.

   b) Use three sinusoidal (Comm> Signal Sources) as carriers at frequencies 10Hz, 20Hz, and 30Hz to up-convert the different BPSK signals to different frequency band in the frequency spectrum.

   c) Use multiplier block (Blocks>Arithmetic > *) to multiply the BPSK signals with the carriers for up-conversion.

   d) Use the summing junction block (Block> Arithmetic > summing junction) and add the three up-converted signals to obtain the FDMA signal. Add one input to the summing junction or use two summing junctions with two inputs each. See also Lab 2.

   e) Use the spectrum block real (Comm> Operators> Spectrum real) to obtain the spectrum of the combined BPSK signals. Set the following for this unit:

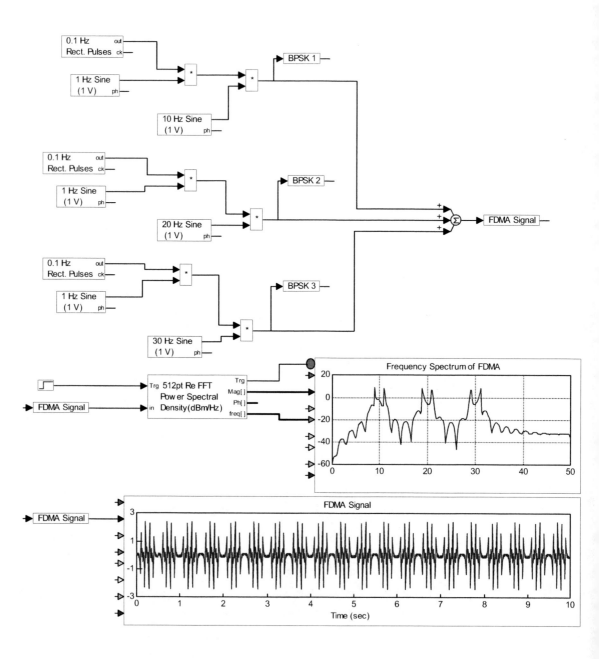

Trigger mode: Continuous

Spectral Output: Mag/Phase   FFT window type: Rectangular

FFT size: 512   Power Spectrum Unit: dBm/Hz

Load: 50 ohms   Output Frequency unit: Hz

f) Connect the Spectrum analyzer block to display. Use the following setting for the display unit.

Fixer Bound

External trigger: 0;

XY Plot X=axis: 4

Axis

Y-Upper Bound: 20   X-Upper Bound: 50

Y-Lower Bound: -60   X- Lower Bound: 0

g) In order to avoid crowded wires use variable (Blocks> Annotation>variable) and name them properly. Connect it to the output of summing junction and name it FDMA signal

h) Simulate the circuit, and run the design. Use the following simulation properties

System > System Properties

Frequency: 100   Hz

End: 10

Conclusion/Observation

1. Working of the FDMA system is studied.

2. What will be the effect if the different up-converter frequencies are close to one another?

3. What will be the effect if the bandwidth of the BPSK signals is greater than the frequency separation between the up-converter frequencies?

4. Measure the peak values of frequencies in the output plot of the spectrum analyzer. For this measurement use the same procedure in the previous exercise. Are these frequencies the same as your expectation?

5. Write down your observation and explain the operation of the system and prepare a copy for your instructor

Exercise 3

Objective

- Study, simulate, and analyze the FDMA receiver system using VisSim.
- Demodulate the BPSK signals and recover the original digital data signals.

Lab Setup

Standard lab setup with VisSim installed

Introduction

The FDMA receiver system along with the transmitter and demodulation is studied in this exercise. The received combined signal is given to each of the down-converting blocks that recover the base-band signals. First the combined signal is multiplied with each of the carrier signals and also by BPSK modulation sinusoid signal. Then an integrator and dump is used to extract the data.

The goal is to recover the individual BPSK signals and digital data at the FDMA receiver system.

Procedure

1. Simulate the following system using VisSim. Note that the simulation uses the diagram of previous exercise as transmitter. Use the following blocks:

    a) In the receiver use three different carriers to down-convert the signals back to their 1Hz frequency by multiplying (Blocks>Arithmetic>Multiplier) it to the transmitter output. The carriers are 10Hz, 20 Hz and 30 Hz. as in the transmitter.

    b) Use variables (Blocks>Annotation>variable) to connect the output of the transmitter to the different parts of the receiver system to avoid crowded figure.

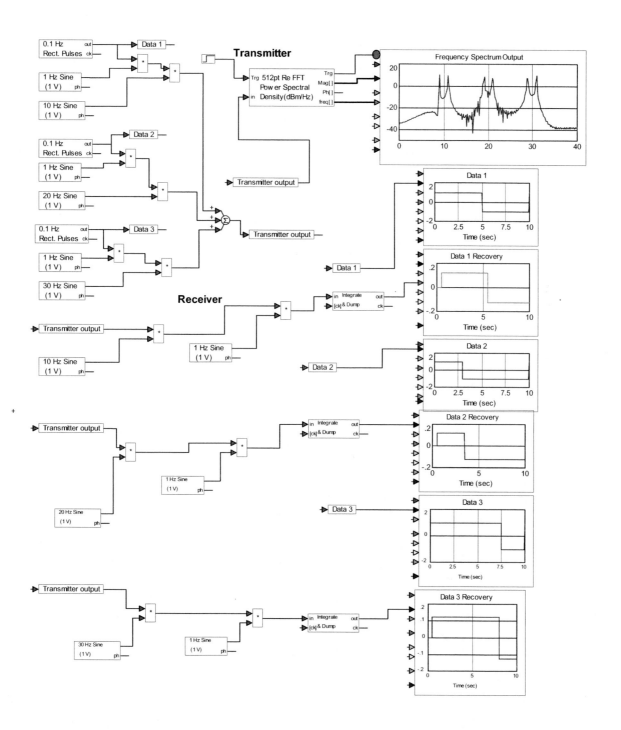

c) In order to recover the data, multiply the output of the first stage multiplier by 1 Hz sinusoid. Then, use an integrator and dump block (Comm > Operators > Integrator and dump (real)) to recover the data. The setting of integrator and dump is as follows:

Dump Timing: Internal	Integrator Method: Euler
Reset value: 0	Scale factor: 1
Output mode: Held	Dump rate (Hz): 2

d) Use different display units to show input data in the transmitter and the demodulated data in the output of the receiver. Adjust the X and Y bounds for a good display.

e) Simulate the circuit, and run the design. Use the following simulation properties

System > System Properties

Frequency: 100   Hz

End: 10

Conclusion and observation

1. What is the effect of multiplying the FDMA signal with any of the carrier signals?

2. Why there is a delay between the transmitted and recovered data.

3. Compare the input data to the transmitter with the recovered data in the receiver. Are they the same?

4. Study the spectrum of the signal in the output of multipliers. Note the frequency components and compare it with your expectation. Use the same setting for spectrum unit as in previous lab

5. Write down your observation and explain the operation of the system and prepare a copy for your instructor...

Lab 13: Satellite Earth Station Transmitter, Transponder, and Earth Station Receiver system

Exercise 1

Objective

- Simulate satellite earth station transmitter system in VisSim.
- Observe and analyze the signals at different blocks of the satellite earth station transmitter system.

Lab Setup

Standard lab setup with VisSim installed.

Introduction

The earth station transmitter for a satellite communication system is simulated in this exercise. The original baseband signal is first BPSK modulated. The output of the BPSK modulator is passed through a band-pass filter to remove any out-of-band harmonics and noise. The signal is then up-converted to high frequency, usually 6 GHz or 14 GHz. These are the common uplink frequencies used. Once again, the output of the up-converter is passed through a band- pass filter centered around the up-converter frequency. The output from the band-pass filter is then given to the high-power amplifier which provides the necessary high powers required in satellite communications. The output of the high-power amplifier is sent into the channel using an antenna system.

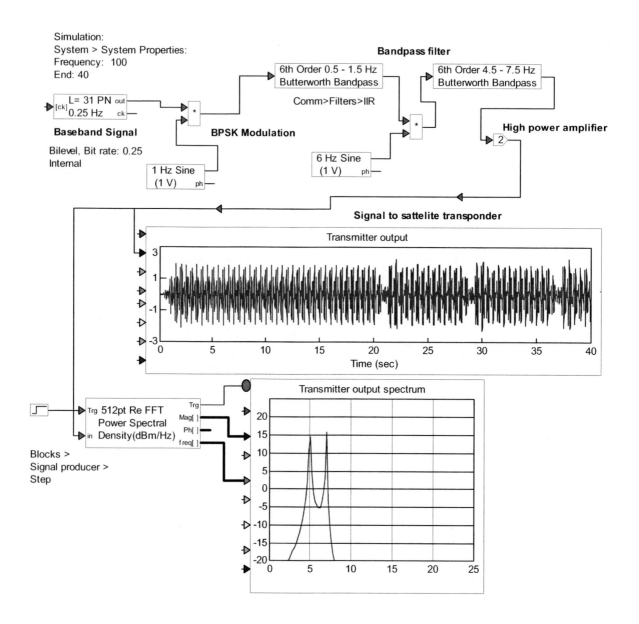

Simulation:
System > System Properties:
Frequency: 100
End: 40

Bandpass filter

6th Order 0.5 - 1.5 Hz
Butterworth Bandpass

Comm>Filters>IIR

6th Order 4.5 - 7.5 Hz
Butterworth Bandpass

[ck] L= 31 PN out
0.25 Hz ck

Baseband Signal

Bilevel, Bit rate: 0.25
Internal

*

BPSK Modulation

*

High power amplifier

2

1 Hz Sine
(1 V) ph

6 Hz Sine
(1 V) ph

Signal to sattelite transponder

Transmitter output

3
1
-1
-3

0   5   10   15   20   25   30   35   40
Time (sec)

Trg 512pt Re FFT
Power Spectral
in Density(dBm/Hz)

Trg
Mag[ ]
Ph[ ]
freq[ ]

Transmitter output spectrum

20
15
10
5
0
-5
-10
-15
-20

0   5   10   15   20   25

Blocks >
Signal producer >
Step

Procedure

1. Set up the circuit as shown in the figure. Use the following blocks:

a) Use a PN sequence (Comm>Signal sources > PN Sequence) code generator as the digital baseband signal generator. Set up the PN code generator as follows:

Shift Register size: 5	Output Mode: Bi-level
Sequence offset: 0	Bit rate bps: 0.25
Initial state (Octal): 37	Start (sec): 0
Timing: Internal	

b) Use a 1Hz sinusoid signal (Comm>Signal sources > Sinusoid) as the BPSK carrier.

c) Use a multiplier (Blocks>Arithmetic > *) as BPSK modulator

d) Since the output of the BPSK signal will be centered around 1Hz, use a band-pass filter centered around 1Hz. You may also use a low-pass filter with cutoff at 2Hz since the carrier is of very low frequency in the simulation. In real systems the frequency of the BPSK carrier will be of the order of MHz.

Use a 6th order Butterworth band-pass filter (Comm> Filters>IIR). Set the lower frequency of the filter 0.5 Hz and the upper frequency to 1.5 Hz.

e) Use a 6 Hz sinusoid as the up-converter frequency. In real-life systems a frequency of 6 GHz or 14 GHz is used as uplink center frequency.

f). Use a 6th order Butterworth band-pass filter centered around 6Hz as the band-pass filter after the up-conversion. Set the lower frequency to 4.5 Hz and Upper frequency to 7.5 Hz. This will remove frequencies that fall out of band especially the harmonics.

g). A simple gain block (Blocks>Arithmetic > gain) is used as the high-power amplifier. Set the gain to 2.

h) The output of the amplifier is the actual output of the ground station earth transmitting system that is sent up the channel. The channel is considered free space and Line- Of - Site (LOS) to the satellite transponder.

i) To see the spectrum of the output signal connect the output of the gain block to spectrum analyzer unit. Set the following for this unit:

Spectrum analyzer real: (Comm> Operators > Spectrum analyzer (real))

Trigger mode: Trigger

Spectral Output: Mag /Phase

FFT window type: Rectangular

FFT size: 512

Power Spectrum Unit: dBm/Hz

Load: 50 ohms

Output Frequency: Hz

j) Connect the Spectrum analyzer block to display. Use the following setting for this unit:

Fixed bound

External trigger: 0   Trigger output is connected to input #0 of the plot

XY Plot X=axis: 4   Frequency output of spectrum block is connected to input #4 of the plot

Axis:

Y Upper bound: 25   X Upper bound: 25

Y Lower bound: -20   X lower bound: 0

k) Use the following simulation properties:

System > System Properties

Frequency: 100   Hz

End: 40

Conclusion/Observation

1. Run the simulation using the initial settings shown above, and measure spectral peak frequency values and compare with your expectation

2. Use a display plot to study output of different blocks of the transmitter and trace the signal

3. The signals at different blocks of the satellite earth station transmitting system are observed and analyzed.

4. What happens if the frequency of the BPSK modulating carrier is close to the up-converter frequency?

5. In realistic systems, where do you think the BPSK carrier and the up-converter find themselves in the frequency spectrum?

6. What will the effect of increasing the order for the Butterworth filter?

7. Prepare a copy of the simulation and your conclusion for your instructor.

Exercise 2

Objective

- Simulate the satellite transponder using VisSim.
- Study the effect of the AWGN channel on the satellite transponder in VisSim.

Lab Setup

Standard lab setup with VisSim installed

Introduction

The signal from the satellite earth station transmitter is sent along the Line- Of- Sight (LOS) channel. This signal travels along the channel and is captured by the satellite transponder.

In this exercise the earth station in Exercise 1 and AWGN (Additive White Gaussian Noise) channel is used to add noise to the signal before reaching the satellite transponder.

The AWGN channel adds white Gaussian noise to the signal. Also, since the travel distance is too high, an additional attenuation factor is included in the path.

The satellite transponder takes the signals peak at 5 Hz and 7 Hz with centered at 6Hz and then multiplies it with the 2Hz signal to change its center frequency. The band-pass filter transmits the signal centered at 4 Hz frequency. This is then given to the high-power amplifier, the output of which is transmitted down to the earth station receiver. Therefore, the transponder acts as a satellite repeater with a frequency transformation from the frequency centered at 6Hz to frequency centered at 4Hz.

Procedure

1. Set up the circuit in VisSim as shown in the following figure. The earth station transmitter that is simulated in the previous exercise is repeated here

a) To avoid crowded lines use variables (Blocks> Annotation> variable) in different units of the system and name them accordingly. In this way it is easy to study the signal trace in different part of the system. For example to see the baseband data, connect the variable called "Data" to the input of the plot.

Earth Station Transmitter

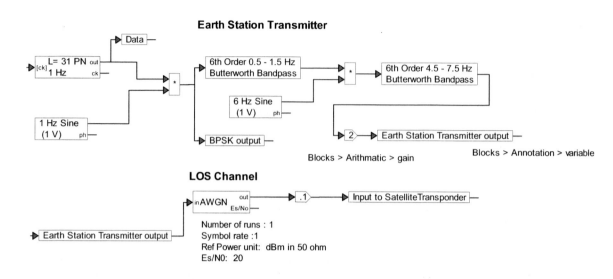

Blocks > Arithmatic > gain   Blocks > Annotation > variable

LOS Channel

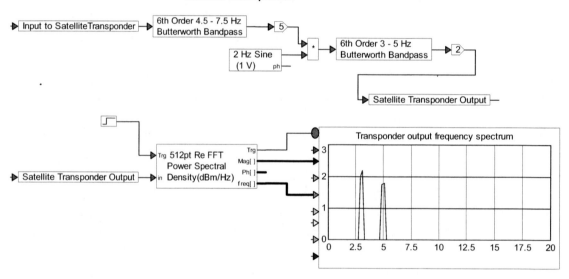

Number of runs : 1
Symbol rate :1
Ref Power unit: dBm in 50 ohm
Es/N0: 20

Satellite Transponder

Transponder output frequency spectrum

b) To simulate the channel, use the AWGN channel block (Comm>Channels > AWGN (real)) and adjust its parameters as follows:

> Number of runs: 1
>
> Symbol rate: 1
>
> Ref. Power unit: dBm in 50 ohm
>
> Es/N0: 20

c) Provide an attenuation block (Blocks>Arithmetic > gain) to simulate the huge attenuation that takes place in satellite communications. Set the attenuation to 0.1

d) Give the output of the channel to the input of the band-pass filter of the transponder as shown in the figure, which is centered about 6Hz. Use a 6th order Butterworth filter (Comm > Filters > IIR). Set the lower frequency of the filter to 4.5 Hz and the upper frequency to 7.5 Hz.

e) Connect the band-pass filter output to the amplifier (Blocks>Arithmetic > gain), Set the gain to 5.

f) In order to convert the frequency to down link frequency, the output of the amplifies is multiply with 2Hz sinusoid (Comm > Signal sources > sinusoid)

f) The resultant signal is connected to a band-pass filter to contain the downlink signal centered about 4 Hz.

g) This signal is amplified before being transmitted down to the earth station receiver. Set the gain to 2.

h) Connect the output of the gain block to Spectrum analyzer unit. Set the following for this unit:

> Spectrum analyzer real: (Comm>Operators > Spectrum analyzer real)

Trigger mode: Trigger	FFT size: 512
Spectral Output: Mag/Phase	Load: 50 ohms
FFT window type: Rectangular	Output Frequency: Hz
Power Spectrum Unit: dBm/Hz	Number of FFT average: 1

i) Connect the Spectrum analyzer block to display. Use the following setting for this unit

> Fixed Bond   Grid line
>
> External trigger: 0;   Trigger output is connected to input #0 of the plot
>
> XY Plot X=axis: 4   Frequency output of spectrum block is connected to input #4 of the plot

Axis:

Y upper bound: 3   X upper bound: 20

Y lower bound: 0   X lower bound: 0

j) Use the following simulation properties:

System > System Properties

Frequency: 100 Hz

End: 10

Conclusion/Observation

1. Run the simulation using the initial settings shown above, and measure spectral peak values and compare with your expectation

2. Use a display plot to study output of different blocks of the transmitter and trace the signal.

3. Check the frequency spectrum of different unit output and compare it with your analysis.

4. Why is the pass-band of the band-pass filter selected to be [4.5–7.5] Hz?

5. Prepare a copy of the simulation and your conclusion for your instructor.

Exercise 3

Objective

- Simulate satellite earth station receiver system in VisSim.
- Observe and analyze the signals at different blocks of the satellite earth station receiver system.

Lab Setup

Standard lab setup with VisSim installed

Introduction

After the frequency translated signal is transmitted from the satellite transponder, the signal travels through the down link channel and is received at the earth station receiver.

The following figure shows the earth station transmitter in Exercise 1, satellite transponder in Exercise 2, satellite earth station receiver and up and down link channels.

The signal that is transmitted by the satellite transponder gets corrupted by AWGN and also attenuated by the time it reaches the earth station receiver. First the received signal is low-pass-filtered to remove the out-of-band frequency components added by the noise. Then the signal is amplified before subject to further processing. It is then down-converted using a carrier signal. The down-converted signal is low-pass-filtered to get the BPSK signal. The BPSK signal is demodulated using a multiplier, an integrator and dump unit

Procedure

1. Set up the circuit, as shown in the following figure. So far we had the earth station transmitter, up link channel, and satellite transponder in previous labs. In this lab only the down link channel and satellite earth station receiver is added. To avoid crowded lines use variables (Blocks>Annotation>variable) in different units of the system and name them accordingly. In this way it is easy to study the trace of the signal in different part of the system. For example to see the baseband data, connect the variable "Data" to the input of the plot.

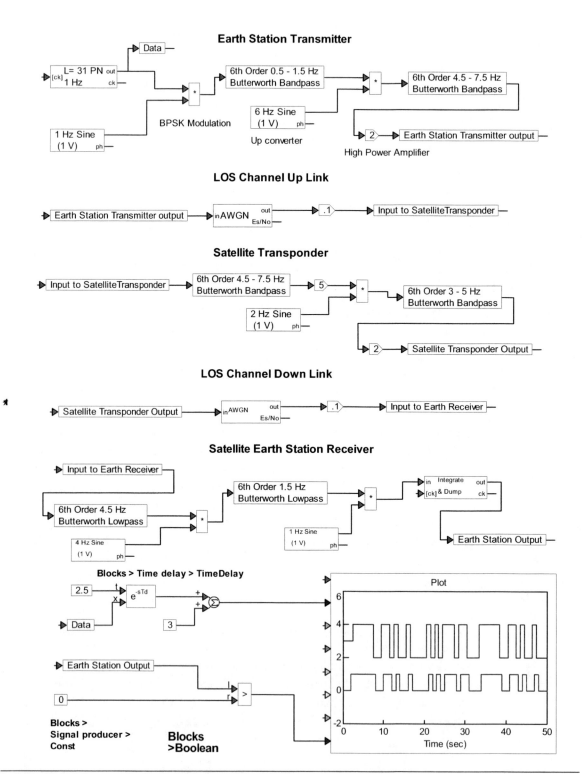

Earth Station Transmitter

Data

L= 31 PN out
[ck] 1 Hz   ck

6th Order 0.5 - 1.5 Hz
Butterworth Bandpass

6th Order 4.5 - 7.5 Hz
Butterworth Bandpass

6 Hz Sine
(1 V)   ph

BPSK Modulation

1 Hz Sine
(1 V)   ph

Up converter

2   Earth Station Transmitter output

High Power Amplifier

LOS Channel Up Link

Earth Station Transmitter output

in AWGN   out
        Es/No

.1

Input to SatelliteTransponder

Satellite Transponder

Input to SatelliteTransponder

6th Order 4.5 - 7.5 Hz
Butterworth Bandpass

5

6th Order 3 - 5 Hz
Butterworth Bandpass

2 Hz Sine
(1 V)   ph

2   Satellite Transponder Output

LOS Channel Down Link

Satellite Transponder Output

in AWGN   out
        Es/No

.1

Input to Earth Receiver

Satellite Earth Station Receiver

Input to Earth Receiver

6th Order 4.5 Hz
Butterworth Lowpass

6th Order 1.5 Hz
Butterworth Lowpass

in Integrate out
[ck] & Dump   ck

4 Hz Sine
(1 V)   ph

1 Hz Sine
(1 V)   ph

Earth Station Output

Blocks > Time delay > TimeDelay

2.5   t
       e^-sTd
       x

Data

3

+
+
Σ

Plot

Earth Station Output

0

>

Blocks >
Signal producer >
Const

**Blocks
>Boolean**

Time (sec)

a) To simulate the channel, use the AWGN channel block (Comm>Channels > AWGN (real)) and adjust its parameters as follows:

Number of runs: 1

Symbol rate: 1

Ref. Power unit: Watts in 50 ohm

E_s/N_0: 20

b) Provide an attenuation block (Blocks>Arithmetic> Gain) to simulate the huge attenuation that takes place in satellite communications. Set gain to 0.1.

c) Give the output of the down link channel to the input of the low-pass filter of the earth station receiver as shown to remove out-of-band noise. Use a 6th order low-pass Butterworth filter (Comm> Filters> IIR). Set the cutoff frequency to about 4.5Hz

d) Then the low-pass filter output is frequency down converted by multiplying with a carrier of 4Hz.

e) The resultant signal is connected to a low-pass filter to pass the signal lower than about 1.5 Hz. The result is BPSK signal

f). Use a 1Hz sinusoid (Comm>Signal sources) signal as the BPSK carrier

g) Use the multiply block (Blocks > Arithmetic > *) to multiply the sinusoid 1 Hz to the output of the filter.

g). Connect the output of the multiplier to integrate and dump unit (Comm > Integrate and dump real). The settings for this unit are:

Dump timing: Internal	Reset value: 0
Scale factor: 1	Integration method: Euler
Output Mode: Held	Dump rate (Hz): 1
Initial Delay: 0	

h) Connect the output of integrator and dump to a less than decision box (Blocks > Boolean). These two units extract the original data. The decision box compares the output to zero and generates the data as zero or one.

i) In order to compare the transmitted data and the received data a delay block (Blocks > Time Delay > TimeDelay) is used before the plot. Also a 3 unit is added to that in order to separate the two plots from each other.

j) Use the following setting for the plot

Fixed Bound

Axis:

Y Upper bound: 6   X Upper bound: 50

Y lower bound: -2   X lower bound: 0

i)   Use the following simulation properties:

System > System Properties

Frequency: 1000   Hz

End: 50

Conclusion/Observation

1. Run the simulation and plot the graph of base band signal of earth station transmitter (Data) and compare it with the earth station receiver output.

2. Use plot to study the signals at different blocks of the satellite earth station receiver system and trace the signal.

3. What is the effect of increasing the order of band-pass filter?

4. What is the effect of decreasing signal to noise ratio in AWGN unit. For example set E_b/N_0 to 10 and see if error occurs.

5. Why is a low-pass filter used instead of a band-pass filter in the simulation?

6. Prepare a copy of the simulation and your conclusion for your instructor.

Lab 14: Baseband DSSS Transmitting and Receiving Systems

Objective

- Simulate the baseband Direct Sequence Spread Spectrum (DSSS) transmitting system in VisSim.
- Simulate the baseband DSSS receiving system in VisSim.
- Study the working of the baseband DSSS transmitting and receiver systems in VisSim.
- Observe the effect of using a different PN code at the receiver for the recovery of the data.

Lab Setup

Standard lab setup with VisSim installed

Introduction

In baseband DSSS transmitting system the low bit rate digital data is directly multiplied with the relatively high chip rate PN code. This multiplication causes the signal to spread in its frequency spectrum. The resulting spread spectrum output is transmitted into the channel. At the receiver end, the received signal is directly multiplied with the same PN code that is used at the transmitter, yielding recovery of the digital data. If a PN code other than the one used at the transmitter is used at the receiver end, then the signal decoded will appear as noise. A VisSim diagram of the baseband DSSS transmitter and receiver system is shown in the following figure.

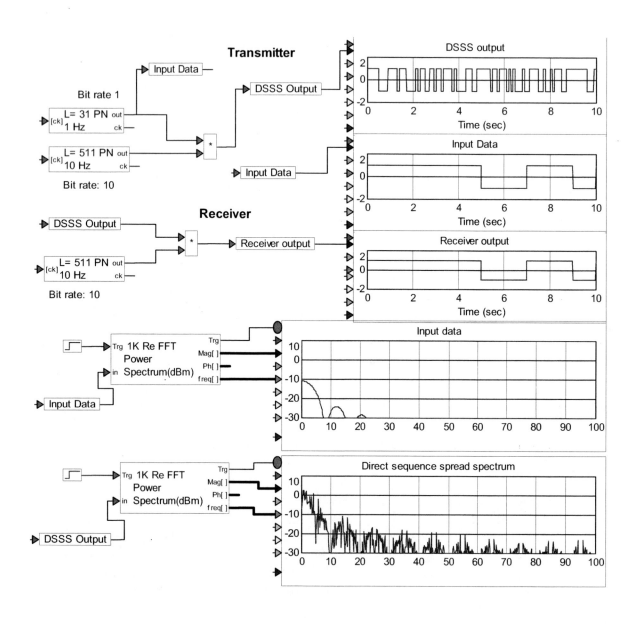

Procedure

1. Set up the circuit in VisSim as shown.

a) Use a PN code generator (Comm>Signal sources >PN sequence) as the digital data source. Set it as follows :

Shift register size: 5	Bi-level (-1, 1)
Timing: Internal	Sequence offset: 0
Initial state (Octal): 37	Bit rate: 1
Start time: 0	

b) Use another PN code generator block to generate the high bit rate spreading code. Set it as follows:

Shift register size: 9	Bi-level (-1, 1)
Timing: Internal	Sequence offset: 0
Initial state (Octal) 37	Bit rate: 10
Start time: 0	

c) Connect the digital data and the PN code data to the multiplier unit (Blocks>Arithmetic > *) to generate the DSSS output.

d) At the baseband DSSS receiver system, multiply the received signal with the same PN code and the same bit rate used at the transmitting end.

e) Use variables (Blocks>Annotations>Variable) to avoid crowded wiring and name them properly.

f) Observe the time domain of the baseband digital signal, the PN code, and the DSSS data.

g) Use the real-spectrum analyzer block (Comm>Operators>Spectrum real>) to observe the spectrum of the signals. Set the following settings for this unit:

Trigger mode: Continuous	Spectral Output: Mag/Phase
FFT window type: Rectangular	FFT size: 1K
Power Spectrum Unit: dBm	Output frequency: Hz
Load: 50 ohms	

h) Connect the Spectrum analyzer block to display unit. Use the following setting for the plot unit.

Fixer Bound

External trigger: 0;	Trigger out put connected to input #0
XY Plot X axis: 4	Frequency is connected to input #4

Y-Upper Bound: 10   X-Upper Bound: 100
Y- Lower Bound: -30   X- Lower Bound: 0

i) Simulate the circuit, and run the design. Use the following simulation properties.

System > System Properties

Frequency: 200   Hz
End: 10

Conclusion/Observation

1. Observe the output and plot the graphs of input data, received signal, DSSS output and compare the frequency spectrum of the data and DSSS output

2. To study the output received by an unintended signal trapper, use a PN code different from the one used by the transmitter end to decode the received signal. Analyze your observation.

3. What happens to the spectrum of the digital signal after multiplication with the spreading code?

4. What is the effect of re-multiplying the spread spectrum signal with the same PN code at the receiver? How does the spectrum of the resulting product signal compare with the original digital signal spectrum?

5. What is the effect of using a different PN code at the receiver?

6. How does the spectrum of the de-spread signal using the incorrect PN code? compare with that of the original digital signal?

7. Print the result and write down your conclusion for your instructor.

Lab 15: BPSK DSSS Transmitting and Receiving Systems

Objective

- Simulate the BPSK DSSS transmitting system in VisSim.
- Simulate the BPSK DSSS receiving system in VisSim.
- Study the working of BPSK DSSS transmitting and receiving systems in VisSim.

Lab Setup

Standard lab setup with VisSim installed

Introduction

The baseband DSSS studied in the previous lab is seldom used. The BPSK DSSS is the most commonly used DSSS system in modern digital communication systems.

For BPSK modulation an additional carrier block is used to modulate the digital data. Then this BPSK-modulated signal is multiplied with the high bit rate spreading code. The multiplication with the PN code can be done either before or after BPSK modulation of the data. In this lab, the digital data is first BPSK modulated before the spreading code is applied.

A block diagram of the BPSK DSSS Transmitter and receiver system is shown in the following figure. Since the PN code is multiplied at a later stage in the transmitting system, the received signal is first de-spread using the PN code. The resulting signal is then BPSK demodulated using integrates and dump block in the BPSK receiver.

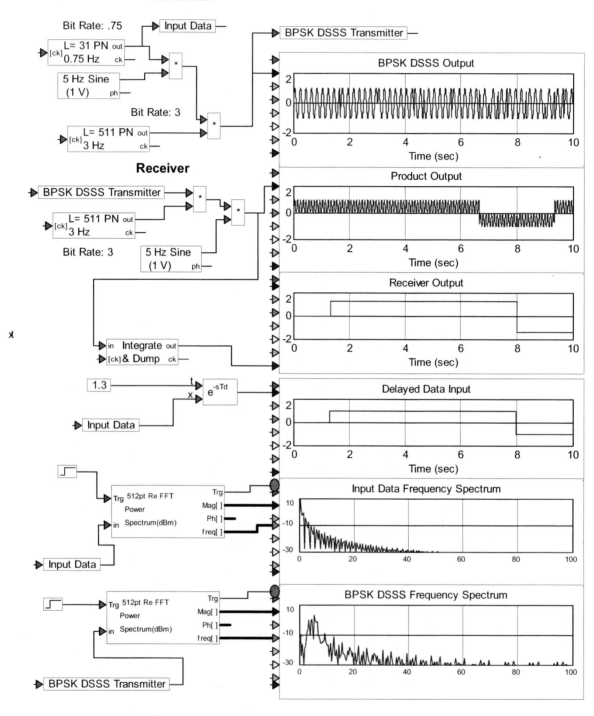

Transmitter

Bit Rate: .75

Input Data

L= 31 PN out
[ck] 0.75 Hz ck

5 Hz Sine
(1 V) ph

Bit Rate: 3

L= 511 PN out
[ck] 3 Hz ck

BPSK DSSS Transmitter

BPSK DSSS Output

Receiver

BPSK DSSS Transmitter

L= 511 PN out
[ck] 3 Hz ck

Bit Rate: 3

5 Hz Sine
(1 V) ph

Product Output

in Integrate out
[ck] & Dump ck

Receiver Output

1.3   t
             e^{-sTd}
             x

Input Data

Delayed Data Input

Trg 512pt Re FFT
     Power
in   Spectrum(dBm)

Trg
Mag[ ]
Ph[ ]
freq[ ]

Input Data Frequency Spectrum

Input Data

Trg 512pt Re FFT
     Power
in   Spectrum(dBm)

Trg
Mag[ ]
Ph[ ]
freq[ ]

BPSK DSSS Frequency Spectrum

BPSK DSSS Transmitter

Procedure

1. Set up the circuit in VisSim as shown in the figure.

   a) Use a PN sequence block (Comm > Signal sources > PN sequence) as the digital data and set it as follows:

Shift register size: 5	Output Mode: Bi-level (-1, 1)
Sequence offset: 0	Initial state (Octal): 37
Timing: Internal	Bit rate (bps): 0.75
Start time (sec): 0	

   b) Use a sinusoid (Comm> Signal sources > sinusoid) of frequency 3 Hz as the carrier for the BPSK modulation.

   c) Multiply the digital data and the carrier to obtain the BPSK-modulated output. The multiplier unit is located at (Blocks> Arithmetic >*).

   d) Multiply the high bit rate spreading PN code with the BPSK-modulated waveform to obtain the BPSK-DSSS output. Choose the following settings for the PN code.

Shift register size: 9	Output Mode: Bi-level (-1, 1)
Sequence offset: 0	Initial state (Octal): 37
Timing: Internal	Bit rate (bps): 3
Start time (sec): 0	

   e) These steps conclude the basic BPSK DSSS transmitter.

   To simulate the BPSK DSSS receiver system in VisSim follow the steps given below. In order to avoid crowded wires use variables (Blocks>Annotation >Variable) and name them properly.

   f) Give the received signal and the PN code to the multiplier for de-spreading the received signal. Use similar PN sequence for de-spreading as in step (d).

   g) Multiply the carrier signal with the de-spread signal to obtain the product signal. Use similar carrier signal as in step (b) for the product.

   h) Connect this product signal to the integrate-and-dump (Comm>Operators > Integrate and Dump (real)) block to recover the digital data. Use the following settings:

Dump rate: Internal	Integration Method: Euler
Reset value: 0	Scale factor: 2
Output Mode: Held	Dump rate: 0.75

i). In order to compare the original digital data with the demodulated data use a delay unit (Blocks > Time Delay > Timedelay) to delay the input data. This delay is needed because of the delay in the integrate and dump unit. Delay the input data by around 1.3 sec. Use also const block (Blocks > Signal producer > Const) for input to the delay.

j) Use the spectrum block (real) (Comm > Operators> Spectrum real) to obtain the spectrum of the input data and BPSK DSSS signals. Set the following for this unit:

Trigger mode: Continuous	Spectral Output: Mag/Phase
FFT window type: Rectangular	FFT size: 512
Power Spectrum Unit: dBm	Load: 50 ohms
Output Frequency unit: Hz	

k) Connect the Spectrum analyzer block to display. Use the following setting for the display unit.

Fixer Bound

External trigger: 0;	Trigger out put connected to input #0
XY Plot X=axis: 4	Frequency is connected to input #4

Axis

Y-Upper Bound: 10	X-Upper Bound: 100
Y- Lower Bound: -30	X- Lower Bound: 0

l) Simulate the circuit, and run the design. Use the following simulation Properties:

System > System Properties

Frequency: 200 Hz

End: 10

Conclusion/Observation

1. The BPSK DSSS spread spectrum system is simulated and studied in VisSim.
2. Compare the demodulated data with the original digital data.
3. Compare the frequency spectrum of the data and the BPSK DSSS.

   Why does the spectrum of the digital signal not contain a single frequency peak like the BPSK carrier signal?

4. Can you create the demodulator using a correlation block instead of the integrate-and-dump circuit?

5. Print the result and write down your conclusion for your instructor.

Lab 16: Wireless Path with Interference

Objective

1. Simulate wireless propagation between a transmitter and receiver
2. Inject an interference signal and report inter-modulation distortion products.

Lab Setup

Standard lab setup with VisSim installed

Introduction

Multipath affects signals propagating through both wireless and fiber optic. In wireless systems, radio waves can take alternate paths from the transmitter to the receiver. For example, in line-of-site systems there is the direct wave from the transmit antenna to the receive antenna. There can also be alternate paths in which the radio wave will bounce off buildings or water. In fiber optic systems, we have multimode, where the signal generated from a single laser can take alternate paths through the fiber. In all cases, this can have a negative effect on the performance of the communications network.

Interfering signals can also have an effect on wireless networks. In most cases, interfering signals can be filtered out at the front end of the receiver.

However, there are harmonic products and inter-modulation products that can be generated within the bandwidth of the receiver. Inter-modulation products are somewhat similar to harmonics however; they are generated by two signals operating at different frequencies.

In this lab a communications circuit is simulated that operates at 2 MHz. Signal is injected at the receiving antenna to simulate both multipath and interfering signals. Then, the effect of interfering or multipath on performance is observed.

In conclusion, the designer wants to ensure an adequate receive signal level to maintain the expected BER, or better. However, just taking into account all the gains and losses in a network may not be adequate to determine if enough signal is available in the receiver. The designer also needs to consider the effects of multipath and interfering signals. A multipath signal can either add to, or decrease from, the primary signal. In practice, a multipath signal will do both at different instances in time. We need to take into account worse case conditions when the interfering signal will be 180 degrees out of phase. Therefore, the designer will have to take this into account by added margin required for the signal-to-noise ratio. The negative effect of multipath can be compensated for by either more gain in the network or by diversity. There are three primary forms of diversity used, including space, frequency, and polarization.

Procedure

1. Construct a wireless system using the following figure in VisSim.

   Use the following parameters:

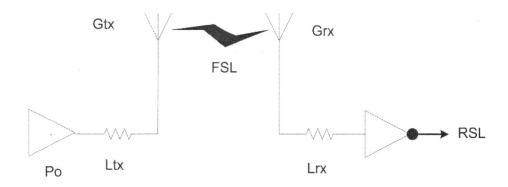

   Po = 6 dBm: Output power of the transmitter

   Ltx = 1.5 dB: Transmitter feeder loss

   Gtx = 3 dB: Transmitter antenna gain

   Grx = 3 dB: Receiver antenna gain

   Lrx = 2 dB: Receiver feeder loss

   FSL: Free space loss based on a 10-mile link

   Receiver gain: 50 dB

   2MHz sinusoidal signal source

2. It is better to search through the various blocks available in VisSim and come up with your own design and compare yours with the following design.

3. Set up the circuit as shown in the following figure in VisSim. Use the following blocks.

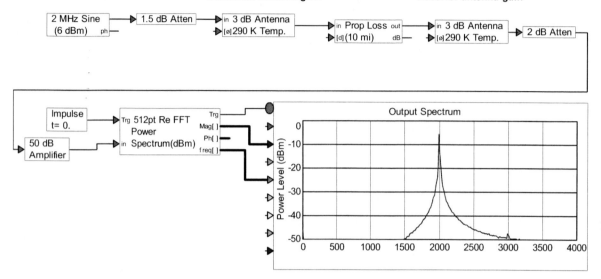

a) Sine Source: (Comm> Signal Sources > Sinusoid)

    Frequency: 2MHz,   Unit: dBm

    Output power: 6dBm   Initial Phase (deg): 0

    Output mode: Sine   Phase output Mode: Unwrapped

b) Use attenuator as transmitter and receiver feeder loss (Comm> RF > Attenuator).This block implements a passive RF attenuator.

c) Use Antenna (Comm > RF > Antenna) for modelling of the antenna gain and noise temperature specification. This block can also model as noiseless. Set the following for this unit:

    Bore sight Antenna gain (dB): 3

    Gain Mode: Fixed

    Noise Temp (K): 290

    Click Add Noise

d) Propagation Loss (Comm> Channels > Propagation loss). Set the following properties:

    Path distance (mi): 10

Frequency (MHz): 2

Distance Mode: Internal

Distance Unit: miles

e) Spectrum analyzer real: (Comm > Operators > Spectrum analyzer (real)))

Trigger mode: Trigger

Spectral Output: Mag/Phase

FFT window type: Rectangular

FFT size: 512

Power Spectrum Unit: dBm

Load: 50 ohms

Output Frequency: KHz

f) Connect an Impulse block (Comm > Signal Sources > Impulse) to trigger the spectrum analyzer block

g) Set the plot as follows:

External trigger: 0;	Trigger out put connected to input #0
XY Plot X=axis: 4	Frequency is connected to input #4

Axis

Y-upper: 0	X-upper: 4000
Y-Lower: -50	X-lower: 0

h) Use the following simulation properties:

System > System properties

Frequency: 7 MHz

End: 0.01

4. Run the simulation using the initial settings shown above, and record spectral information

5. Measure RSL (Received Signal Level) with a spectrum analyzer output by clicking the read coordinate on the plot properties. Compare your measurement with your calculation

6. Referring to the following figure inject a 2 MHz signal at –50 dBm and zero phase shift, at the receiving antenna to simulate interference. Use a sine source and an RF combiner for this purpose. The RF combiner can be found in **Comm > RF > Splitter / combiner**. Open properties and click combiner. Set no additional loss and use two inputs.

7. Record the difference in spectrum on both the primary and harmonic frequencies.

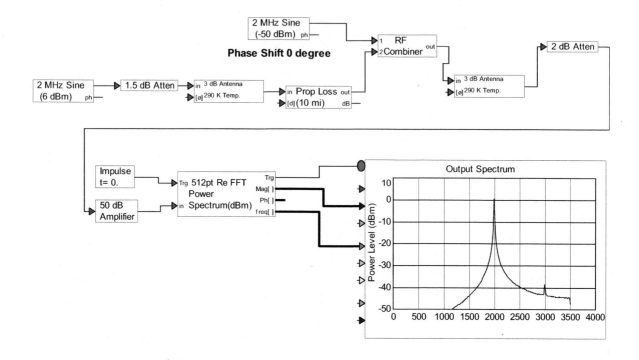

8. Change the phase shift of the interference signal to 180 degrees and record amplitudes of primary and harmonics.

9. Change the phase back to zero degrees. Then change the frequency of the interference signal to 2.5 MHz. Record frequency and signal amplitudes for each peak in the spectrum.

10. Print the result and write down your conclusion for your instructor.